Texts from

OTHER CULTURES

Edited by RACHEL REDFORD

OXFORD
UNIVERSITY PRESS

OXFORD
UNIVERSITY PRESS

Great Clarendon Street, Oxford OX2 6DP

© Rachel Redford 2000
The moral rights of the author have been asserted
Database right Oxford University Press (maker)

First published 2000

ISBN 0 19 831465 5

Cover illustration: Image Bank/Todd Davidson
The maps are by Jeff Edwards
Printed in Great Britain

ACKNOWLEDGEMENTS

We are grateful for permission to reprint the following copyright material:

Mulk Raj Anand: extract from *Coolie* (Penguin Books India, 1993), copyright © Mulk Raj Anand 1936, reprinted by permission of the author. **Sandra Braude**: extract from *Mpho's Search* (Oxford University Press Southern Africa, 1994), copyright © Sandra Braude 1994, reprinted by permission of the publisher. **Pang-Mei Natasha Chang**: extract from *Bound Feet and Western Dress* (Doubleday, a division of Random House Inc, 1996, and Corgi, a division of Transworld Publishers, 1997) copyright © Pang-Mei Natasha Chang, 1996, 1997, reprinted by permission of the publishers. All rights reserved. **Vincent Cronin**: extract from *The Last Migration* (The Reprint Society Ltd, by arrangement with Rupert Hart-Davis, 1959), reprinted by permission of Lady Hart-Davis. **Anita Desai**: extract from *Feasting, Fasting* (Chatto & Windus, 1999), copyright © Anita Desai 1999, reprinted by permission of the author c/o Rogers Coleridge and White, 20 Powis Mews, London, W11 1JN. **Jason Elliot**: extract from *An Unexpected Light: Travels in Afghanistan* (Picador, 1999), copyright © Jason Elliot 1999, reprinted by permission of Macmillan Publishers Ltd. **Buchi Emecheta**: extract from *The Bride Price* (Allison and Busby Ltd, 1976), copyright © Buchi Emecheta 1976, reprinted by permission of the author. **Sattareh Farman Farmaian**: extract from *Daughter of Persia* (Bantam Press, a division of Transworld Publishers, 1992), copyright © Sattareh Farman Farmaian with Dona Munker 1992, reprinted by permission of Transworld Publishers and Abner Stein. All rights reserved. **Eugenie Fraser**: extract from *The House by the Dvina* (Mainstream Publishing Company Ltd, 1984), copyright © Eugenie Fraser 1984, reprinted by permission of the publisher. **Barbara Kingsolver**: extract from *The Poisonwood Bible* (Harper Collins, 1998), copyright © Barbara Kingsolver 1999, reprinted by permission of Frances Golding Literary Agency Inc. **Adeline Yen Mah**: extract from *Falling Leaves Return to Their Roots: The True Story of An Unwanted Chinese Daughter* (Michael Joseph, 1997), copyright © Adeline Yen Mah 1997, reprinted by permission of Penguin Books Ltd. **Ved Mehta**: extract from *Vedi* (OUP Inc, 1981, first published in The New Yorker), copyright © Ved Mehta 1981, reprinted by permission of the author. **Kenzaburo Oë**: extract from *Nip the Buds, Shoot the Kids* translated by Paul St John Mackintosh and Maki Sugiyama (Marion Boyars Publishers Ltd, 1995), copyright © Kenzaburo Oë 1958, English translation copyright © Marion Boyars Publishers 1995, reprinted by permission of the publisher. **Jetsun Pema**: extract from *Tibet: My Story* (Element Books Ltd, 1997) first published as *Tibet, mon histoire* (Editions Ramsay, 1996), translated by Geraldine Le Roy and James Mayor, translation copyright © Element Books Limited, 1997, original text copyright © Editions Ramsay, 1996, reprinted by permission of the publishers. **Ruri Pilgrim**: extract from *Fish of the Seto Inland Sea* (HarperCollins Publishers Ltd, 1999), copyright © Ruri Pilgrim 1999, reprinted by permission of the publisher. **Mira Stout**: extract from *One Thousand Chestnut Trees* (Flamingo, 1997), copyright © Mira Stout 1997, reprinted by permission of HarperCollins Publishers Ltd. **Edith Velmans**: extract from *Edith's Book* (Viking, 1998), copyright © Edith Velmans 1998, reprinted by permission of Penguin Books Ltd. **Vitali Vitaliev**: extract from *Borders Up* (Simon & Schuster Ltd, 1999), copyright © Vitali Vitaliev 1999, reprinted by permission of the publisher.

Contents

Searching for Baba
South Africa

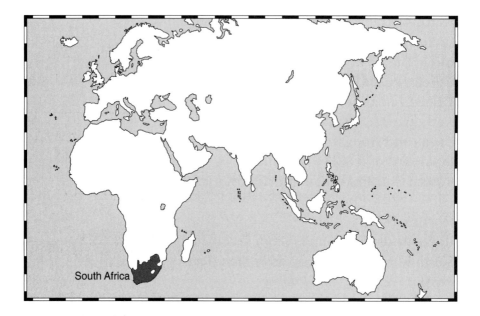

Introduction for the Teacher

In *Mpho's Search* by Sandra Braude, Mpho is a twelve-year-old black boy employed by a white Afrikaner farmer in the Transvaal in South Africa to look after the sheep. His mother died when he was a baby, and he was cared for by his grandmother. Mpho's wages were a little food and the room he and his grandmother lived in. His father went long ago to Johannesburg to work in the mines so he could send some money home, and for Mpho he is merely a distant memory.

At the beginning of the story, Mpho's grandmother has been dead for six months, and Mpho is in desperate trouble. Baas du Toit, the farmer, has told Mpho to leave: sheep are being stolen and baas du Toit blames the innocent Mpho. He gives the boy fifty rand and tells him to leave.

Mpho's only hope is to find Baba, his father, in iGoli (Johannesburg). Not appreciating how hopeless a task that will be in such a vast and dangerous city, he sets off with a little food in a satchel and his blanket with animals on it which has been his only comfort. After a long truck drive he is told to get a taxi to iGoli, but his precious store of money is diminishing. The taxi leaves him in Soweto, the vast shanty town for black South Africans to the south west of

[4]

the city. Bewildered, he sits down to eat the only food he has with him. The story takes place during a momentous time in South Africa's history, in 1994 when the first democratic elections were held, which resulted in Nelson Mandela being elected the first black President of South Africa.

Mpho's Search

It was not long before the taxi stopped, and Mpho got out with the rest of the passengers. Yes, as the old woman had told him, this place was much bigger than Witbank.

'Is this *iGoli?*' he asked the taxi-driver, who laughed.

'This is Soweto,' he said, and pointed to the distance, where tall buildings were framed against the darkening sky. 'That is *iGoli.*'

'How do I get there?' asked Mpho.

'By train or bus or taxi,' said the driver. 'You can go tomorrow. Tonight you had better stay in Soweto.'

Mpho was tired and he did not argue. He would find a place to sleep, but first he wanted to eat some sardines and drink the Coca-cola.

He looked around him. There was a great deal of noise, and people everywhere. They were getting out of taxis and buses. It seemed that nobody stood still. Everyone was walking very fast. There were a lot of people selling things – mainly food. Near where Mpho stood, a woman was selling fruit – apples, oranges, bananas – divided into little piles on tin plates. She was shouting loudly, 'One rand a plate! One rand a plate!' A little further away there was a cart with sausages sizzling on a fire. They smelled very good to Mpho, but he thought he had better keep the rest of his money and eat what he had.

He put his parcels on the ground and, sitting down next to them, took out a tin of sardines and his pocket knife. Opening the tin was harder than he thought, and he had to give the job all his concentration.

Suddenly he heard a noise. Someone was shouting, 'Stop, thief!' and there was the sound of running feet. He looked up and again heard the words, 'Stop thief!' being shouted close to him. He saw the tall, handsome man from the taxi running fast into the crowd. Then he looked down and saw that the bundle with his precious blanket was missing.

'My blanket,' he gasped. 'That man has stolen my blanket!'

Mpho could scarcely keep himself from crying. His blanket was gone!

'My blanket! My lovely blanket! That awful man stole it! I knew he was bad! What shall I do?'

Mpho decided then and there that, whatever happened, he would act like a man. 'I won't cry,' he promised himself. 'I'll just do what I have to, and find *Baba*. But now I must eat my sardines.' He no longer felt like eating, but knew that food must not be wasted. So he pulled his satchel closer to him – he wasn't prepared to lose anything else – and ate the greasy little fish with his fingers. When that was done, he finished off the Coca-cola, and packed the bottle carefully in the satchel. Then he thought, 'I must find a place to sleep. Tomorrow I will begin my search.'

A lot of people were walking in one direction, and Mpho decided to follow them. He didn't know anything at all about where he was going, but was sure that something would turn up.

As soon as he left the place that seemed to be a terminus for taxis, the roads were no longer tarred. They became increasingly narrow, and were dusty and full of holes. This did not worry Mpho, because he was used to country roads. Nor did he mind the fact that soon there were no street-lights, because he was used to walking by moonlight on the farm.

At first he could see that there were big shops lining the road, with great big advertisements on the walls. After this the houses started. They were not as big as the house on baas du Toit's farm, but they were solid, and made out of brick. Each one had a little yard, but there was very little growing there, except for the odd patch of mealies. Mpho thought that, if he lived in one of those houses, he would make a lovely garden, with peach-trees and vegetables growing in it.

As he walked, following the crowd, the houses became smaller and poorer, and these houses didn't even have yards. Some of the people went into the houses, and turned up side-streets, but Mpho followed those who were walking on.

At last he saw where they were going. There was a big, dusty space, and on it were built little *khayas*[1]. These were like the *khayas* where the people who had stolen baas du Toit's sheep lived. They were made of bits of corrugated iron and black plastic bags. Some of them were even made with pieces of wood, or cardboard boxes. They looked as if they would fall down if you blew on them.

There were lots of people sitting outside the *khayas*, some on wooden chairs, some on tomato boxes. They were talking and laughing. There were many children, too. They did not look very clean, and were poorly dressed. Mpho saw one tiny little boy, with huge eyes, dressed only in a ragged shirt, his little bottom sticking out. Most of the men were drinking beer. There were not many women to be seen.

'They must be inside the *khayas* preparing food,' thought Mpho.

One of the women looked like *Gogo*[2]. She was old and had a pleasant face. Mpho missed his grandmother, and was sure that all old women were as nice as she was. So he walked up to her.

'*Mama*,' he said to her, 'I want somewhere to sleep.'

'Where do you come from, and where are your mother and father?' she asked him.

'I come from the farm,' answered Mpho. 'I have come to *eGoli* to look for my father. My mother is dead, and so is *Gogo*. I am tired, *mama*, and must sleep.'

The old woman thought hard. 'You do not look like a *tsotsi*[3],' she said. 'You can sleep in my house, but you must help me, because I am old and am not strong any more. You can leave your things with me. I will look after them and they will be safe. Then you must go and fetch water from the tap. Bring it in that can over there.'

Mpho did as he was told. He took the can and went to where the tap was. There was a long queue waiting for water, and it took a long time before Mpho was able to reach the tap and fill the can. He listened to what the others in the queue were saying, and

---

[1] *khaya*: poor dwelling
[2] *Gogo*: Grandma
[3] *tsotsi*: thug

learned that there were only a few taps here in the camp, and that people sometimes had to wait for many hours to get water. He also learned that the people in the camp were desperately poor and that most of them did not have jobs. But they did not seem unhappy. They spoke together and laughed, and they believed that tomorrow would bring something better.

When Mpho had eventually filled the can, he carried it carefully back to the *khaya*, trying to spill as little of it as possible. The old woman was very pleased.

'You are a good boy,' she said to him. 'I shall cook some water and make pap[1]. You must eat some, then I will show you where you can sleep.'

Mpho's day had been very tiring and he would rather have gone straight to sleep. But he did not want to offend the old woman, so he sat quietly and watched while she made the pap on a little paraffin stove. While they were eating the old woman noticed Mpho looking around.

She said, 'I see you looking at the houses here. They are poor houses, but this is our home. We have nowhere else to live. So we make our houses as nice as we can. My son helped me build my house. He brought me iron and bricks, and he built it for me.' She raised her head proudly. 'He comes to see me, and he always brings me something – food or something.' After this they continued their meal in silence.

At last she said, 'Now I will show you where you can sleep.' She led the way into the *khaya*. There was very little furniture, but everything was spotlessly clean. Newspapers were laid out on the floor, like a carpet. A bed stood against one wall, and against another there were wooden boxes, with a plank of wood across them, to form a shelf, on which a few pots and mugs stood. Pictures cut from magazines were stuck on the walls, and the place looked pretty in the glow of the candle the old woman lit.

'There are newspapers under the bed,' she told Mpho. 'You can take them and make a bed for yourself over there.'

Mpho did as he was told. He did not think he would be able to

---

[1] pap: porridge

sleep on just a pile of newspapers, but after all they were warm and not uncomfortable. As soon as he lay down he fell fast asleep. But it was not a restful sleep. He dreamed, and images flitted across his mind. He saw baas du Toit, so angry, and *Gogo* in the background, shaking her head. He saw the farm, and the windmill, slowly turning. He saw the market-place in Soweto, and the handsome man running away with his blanket, and he heard someone shouting, 'Stop thief! Stop thief!' The shouting grew louder until it woke Mpho and, as he lay on the pile of newspapers, he knew that the shouting was real.

'*Mama*,' he called, but either the old woman was asleep or no longer in the *khaya*. So he shook the sleep out of his head and got up.

Outside the *khaya* there was a lot of activity and noise. People were shouting and running in all directions, like ants when their nest is disturbed.

Then Mpho saw that people were fighting. There were men – big, strong men – armed with sticks and wearing red scarves around their heads. They were very excited, and were hitting people with the sticks. Then more men came. They also carried sticks, but their foreheads were bare. The two groups of men began to fight with each other. Mpho was very frightened. He called again for the old woman, but she was nowhere to be seen.

Now people were running away. They did not want to be caught up in the fighting. A young woman, her head bare, ran past shrieking and clutching her baby tightly.

Mpho saw one of the men run up to a *khaya* and throw something through the door. A few moments later flames reared up through the roof. The *khaya* was on fire! It burned brightly in the dark night. Then the shack next to it caught fire. The shouting grew louder and more intense.

Suddenly there was a new sound. Sirens! As Mpho watched three armoured trucks pulled up at the entrance to the camp. Soldiers, dressed in khaki, jumped out of the trucks. They all wore masks over their faces. They were carrying vicious-looking guns, and they held them ready to shoot.

Sandra Braude

Assignments

1 Describe what happens to Mpho after he gets out of the taxi. What feelings does he experience?

There are two parts to this question. To answer them in detail, you'll need to read the passage carefully and take notes.
We'll start by answering the first part:

What happens to Mpho when he gets out of the taxi?

This question is asking you to **relate** briefly, that is, tell parts of the story. We'll make four headings for you to write under. Relate only the most important parts of the story relevant to each heading:

1 The theft
2 Mpho's exploration of the place
3 Mpho's experiences with the old woman
4 What happened during the night

You could answer the first one this way:

> *After Mpho got out of the taxi, he found himself in a very busy place. He sat down to eat some of the food he had brought with him. As he was concentrating hard on opening the sardine tin with his knife, a man from the taxi stole his blanket and ran off into the crowd.*

When you have related the appropriate four parts of the passage in this way, you are ready to answer the second part of the question:

What feelings does Mpho experience?

To answer this second part of the question, you need to read the passage again. As you read this time, **interpret** Mpho's feelings from his experiences and behaviour.
For example, when Mpho got out of the taxi, there were a great many people, some of them selling things and shouting out. From this, you could **interpret** that Mpho felt confused or perhaps frightened.

From the notes that you make, write some sentences about Mpho's feelings to follow those you have already written on the story. You could add these sentences to those on *The theft* above :

> *Mpho was tired and hungry after his journey. He probably felt overwhelmed by all the noise and the crowds of people but he settled down to eat his sardines in a very sensible way. After his belongings were stolen he was very upset and cried out 'My blanket!', but he forced himself to be brave and refused to cry.*

When you have written like this on Mpho's feelings for each of the headings, you have completed your answer to the question.

2 How does the writer make it clear that the people living in the khayas are poor? Why does the violence happen?

There are two parts to this question. We'll start by answering the first part:

How does the writer make it clear that the people are poor?

Read the part of the passage that describes the khayas, their surroundings and the people that live in them. As you read, make a list of all the evidence that shows that the people and their living conditions are poor.
Your list has been started for you:

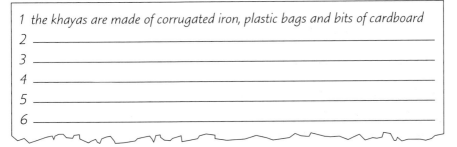

> *1 the khayas are made of corrugated iron, plastic bags and bits of cardboard*
> *2* _____
> *3* _____
> *4* _____
> *5* _____
> *6* _____

When you have completed this list, you will have enough evidence to write a complete paragraph in answer to the first part of the question.

Now you are ready to think about the second part of the question:

Why does the violence happen?

This part of the question is harder! The writer does not tell you the answer, but invites you to think out the answer for yourself using details and information from the passage.

Before writing your answer, it would help to discuss the following questions in a group or with a partner:

⊕ who are the men wearing red scarves?

⊕ why are the men fighting?

⊕ how do the soldiers behave?

Jot down the ideas from your discussion and then use them to write a paragraph on what you think are the reasons for the violence.

Now you have completed the whole question.

Red Letter Days
India/Pakistan

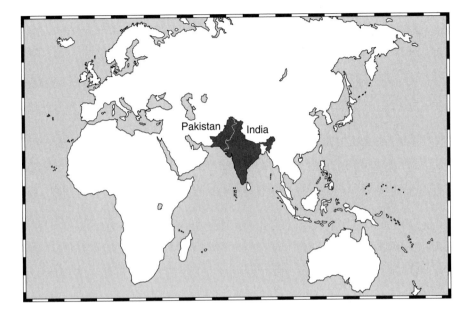

Introduction for the Teacher

This extract comes from a remarkable autobiography. Ved Mehta, now an American scholar and writer, was born in 1934 in an area of what is now Pakistan, but was then part of the Indian Empire ruled by Britain. In 1948 the Indian Empire was divided up under Partition, a time of terrible violent protest, and Pakistan and India became separate countries.

After contracting meningitis at the age of four, Ved was left totally blind. His father was a Hindu doctor and he was determined that his son would not suffer the almost certain fate of blind people in India at that time: begging on the streets. It seems extraordinary to us now, but he sent Vedi thirteen hundred miles away just before he was five years old, to the Dadar School for the Blind in Bombay. Mr Ras Mohun, the school's Principal, had Western ideas about education of which Vedi's father approved. Vedi was to learn English and Braille despite the fact his language was Punjabi and at school the boys, many of whom were street waifs, spoke Marathi. There were concessions for Vedi: he was to have meals with the Principal's family and his bed in the dormitory was a special, comfortable one.

The Principal intended his blind pupils to have as full an education as sighted children – and that included sport and outings. In the following, Ved Mehta describes the school running races and a visit to the beach. The accounts are fascinating not just because they show the Principal's passionately-held ideas about educating blind children, but also because they are written from the standpoint of a blind child absorbing the wonderful freedom of the sea and the sensations of sound and touch that fed his mind.

Vedi

One afternoon, Mr Ras Mohun took those of us boys who were totally blind behind the school building, past Abdul's boa-constrictor tree, to a little vacant area by the wall of the Tata Mill. Here he let us feel four waist-high metal wires and what he called the starting and finishing posts, between which the wires had been strung. The wires formed three long lanes, each a few feet wide. Each wire had a hoop about the size of a thick bangle hanging from it.

'This is a racing track,' he said. 'I have modelled it on a racing track for the blind which I saw at Perkins, in America. We will have races for you here every week.'

We were excited. At school, the most we could do was to run up and down the boys' stairs, and even that we were not supposed to do, because the Sighted Master didn't like the noise we made. When we went for our outings, we had to hold on to the partially sighted or half-sighted boys and walk slowly. But here, Mr Ras Mohun said, we could run, and by ourselves.

Mr Ras Mohun positioned Abdul, Reuben, and me in separate lines, at the starting posts, and showed us how to catch hold of the metal hoop by a string that hung from it, and then run with the wire as our guide.

'No, no, Reuben, don't hold on to the string with both hands,' Mr Ras Mohun said. 'Just catch hold of the string loosely with your right hand, like this.'

'I don't need the string, Uncle,' I said. 'I can run just holding onto the hoop.'

'You need the string for a certain amount of lee-way,' he said. 'Let's have a trial race, and you'll see what I mean.'

I prayed to Jesus, Mary, and Joseph that I would win.

Mr Ras Mohun called out, 'Ready, steady, go!'

I had never run so fast. I imagined myself an arrow flying from one post to the other.

'Oh, my God, they're going to kill themselves!' I heard Mr Ras Mohun exclaim as I fell sidewise, almost wrapping myself around the finishing post, and hitting my mouth on it.

'Any of you badly hurt?' Mr Ras Mohun asked, running up to us.

All three of us had bleeding mouths and bleeding foreheads. There had been no way for us to know when we were coming to the end, so we had all fallen down and hurt ourselves on the finishing posts.

Mr Ras Mohun sent for tincture of iodine and bandages, and after he had attended to our injuries he said, almost to himself, 'Bless me, I can't remember how they prevented such mishaps at Perkins.' He paused, and then went on, to us, 'I know. I'll station the Sighted Master at the finishing posts with my bell. He can ring it during the races. From the sound of the ringing, you'll know how close you are to the end. As an added precaution, I'll have a nice, strong rope stretched across the lanes, at the height of the wires, just before the end, so that if you fall you won't hit the finishing posts.'

After that, every Saturday we had races at the racing track. Mr Ras Mohun would stand at the starting posts and get us off, and the Sighted Master would stand at the finishing posts, behind the newly stretched rope, and ring the bell. Abdul, Reuben, and I were the three fastest runners, and whenever the school had visitors – missionaries and benefactors, Bombay notables and government officials – we three would be asked to put on a special racing exhibition, running different kinds of races we had learned. We would put on the Biscuit Race: Mr Ras Mohun would give us each a hard biscuit, and when he said 'Ready, steady, go!' we would eat the biscuit quickly, show our mouths to him, and then run. We would put on the Leapfrog Race: we would leap frog-fashion along the racing track, hanging on to the string. We would put on the Dog Race, with two dogs, Bobby and Robby, which Mr Ras Mohun had just acquired for us to play with: Mr Ras Mohun would line up Bobby and Robby as best he could outside the lanes, and we would all race against one another. The Dog Race was not as satisfactory as the Biscuit Race or the Leapfrog Race, because Mr Ras Mohun never quite succeeded in starting Bobby and Robby at the right time and getting them to run exactly as he wanted them to.

As time went on, the boys from a sighted school nearby occasionally came and joined us at our Saturday races. They would run outside the lanes. I was so eager to compete with them on even terms that now and again I would slyly let go of the string and hurl the hoop forward, so that I would run along the track like them for a time.

One warm day, there was a series of explosions at the front gate. At first, I thought someone was setting off firecrackers, but then I realized that what I heard was a motorcar engine idling and repeatedly backfiring. We heard such engine sounds all the time – mixed with the clip-clop of victoria horses, the clatter of handcarts, and the clink and ponk-ponk of bicycle bells and car klaxons – but they were always the sounds of passing traffic. No vehicle, it seemed, ever stopped in front of the school.

'Mr Ras Mohun wants us all at the front gate!' Bhaskar cried, running into the boys' dormitory. 'There's a lorry! We are really going to Juhu Beach!'

We had heard Mr Ras Mohun mention the visit to Juhu Beach as a 'red-letter day'. We had all talked about going to the seaside, without knowing exactly what it was. Abdul had once remarked, 'Mahim Sea Beach is not the seaside, and there is no stuffed sand or stuffed ocean for the blind to feel. They have to take us to Juhu Beach to show us what it is.'

'Why are we going in a lorry?' I asked now.

'Because there are no trams to Juhu Beach, you son of an owl,' Abdul said. 'It's really far.'

The lorry had no seats, so we all sat on the floor, the boys on one side and the girls on the other. I wanted to run around – perhaps to sit with Paran – but Mr Ras Mohun was addressing us from the front of the lorry.

'Boys and girls, this is our first annual holiday at Juhu Beach,' he said. 'Juhu Beach is on the Arabian Sea, and we have a day's holiday there because of a special gift from Mrs Thomas and the American Marathi Mission. I want you to stay in your places, because the ride to Juhu Beach is bumpy.'

To help us pass the time, Miss Mary led us in a new song. It really had only one line: 'John Brown's Whiskey Bottle Number One Hundred and One.' Each time we sang it, we would sing out one number less than the time before. The song sounded naughty and festive to us, and we felt we were really on an annual holiday.

At Juhu Beach, I heard a sound I'd never heard before – a gigantic roar alternating with the sound of a huge amount of water rushing out. The sound was very different from Mahim Sea Beach, which was quiet, like a canal in Lahore. (It was actually an inlet.) I wanted to run towards the sound and touch it – to feel what it was really like – but the Sighted Master herded us boys into the boys' shack. He gave us each a pair of bathing drawers and we got into them.

'Now you can do what you like,' the Sighted Master said. 'But don't go beyond the rope in the water.'

I hesitated for a moment, wondering if there were wired lanes and how, amid the roar and the rush, I would hear the Sighted Master ringing the bell on the other side of the rope, but the partially sighted boys started running toward the roar and the rush, calling back, 'Abdul, Reuben! Vedi! There is nothing in the way! You can run, too!'

I ran toward the roar and the rush. The air smelled of salt and coconut. There was hot, grainy, dry ground underfoot. It was so hot that I could scarcely bear to put my feet on it, so I had to run fast, and couldn't stop to examine it. Suddenly, I was in the water, being carried out. It closed over my head. I forgot everything. I felt I'd never been so happy. A jolt opened my mouth. I was rapidly swallowing water that tasted of tears – buckets of them. I was flung back, choking. Again the water closed over my head. The water retreated. I lay on the water, wondering if the sea could take me all the way to the Punjab. Then I came up against the rope, as thick as the one we used for the tug-of-war, and I heard the Sighted Master calling to me, 'That's far enough! Come back! You'll drown!'

We spent the day bathing in the water and running around on the new ground. I couldn't get over the way it shifted around, almost like the water. We could go into the water as often as we liked, and when we ran we just had to keep the sound of the ocean to our left or right, depending on which way we were facing. The school compound and the racing track suddenly shrank in my mind, like a woollen sock Mamaji had knitted for me which became so small after Heea's ayah washed it that I could scarcely get my hand in it.

Ved Mehta

Assignments

1 What did young Vedi find so exciting about the school races and the trip to the beach?

To make sure that you give a full and detailed answer, we'll divide the question into:
⊕ the school races
⊕ the trip to the beach.

First, read the account of the school races and as you read, jot down the parts of the experience which Vedi found exciting under the following headings:
⊕ how the races compared with the running Vedi could do before
⊕ how the sighted boys extended his enjoyment of running.

When you have finished, use your notes to write a paragraph for each heading. The first one has been completed for you:

> *Before the races, the only running Vedi and the blind boys could do was to run up and down stairs, but this was restricted by the Master who stopped them from doing it because of the noise they made. When Vedi went out walking he had to walk slowly holding onto a boy with more sight than himself. This must have been very frustrating so when Vedi understood how the running track would let him run fast by himself, he was very excited and completely fearless. The new freedom was exhilarating to him.*

When you have completed the paragraph for the other heading, you are ready to go on to the second part of the question:
⊕ the trip to the beach.

Read the account of the trip to the beach and, as you did for the first part, take notes as you read on what made the experience exciting for Vedi, this time under the following headings:
⊕ the lorry and the journey there
⊕ Vedi's first experience of the sea and sand.

Write your notes up into two paragraphs, one under each heading. Now you have completed the whole question.

2 How do the writer's words portray his experiences from the standpoint of a blind child?

Because Vedi is totally blind, rather than seeing with his eyes, he hears, smells and feels his experiences. First of all, we'll find the words which tell you that Vedi is using his senses other than sight. Read through the passage and as you read, make a list of appropriate sentences, words and phrases.

The list has been started for you:

> 1 *running around on the new ground. I couldn't get over the way it shifted*
>   *around, almost like the water.*
>
> 2 _____
>
> 3 _____
>
> 4 _____
>
> 5 _____
>
> 6 _____

When you have completed the list, you will have built up a collection of the words which show Vedi's vivid sense impressions.

Now, you need to answer the 'how' part of the question:

> **How** do the writer's words...

To do this, you need to look closely at the words used in your examples and **explain** how they describe sensations and experiences for a boy who cannot see.
The first one has been completed for you:

> *Vedi calls the sand the 'new ground' because he's never been to a beach before*
> *and has never walked on sand. Calling it 'new ground' stresses how unfamiliar it*
> *is to him. His fascination is conveyed at the way the sand shifts and moves by*
> *the way he describes it as moving like water. He combines the ideas of two*
> *things he knows, 'water' and 'ground', to describe how it feels to walk on this*
> *surface that he's never felt before.*

When you have written the explanations for all your examples in this way, you have completed the whole question.

Uma is Considered of Marriageable Age

India

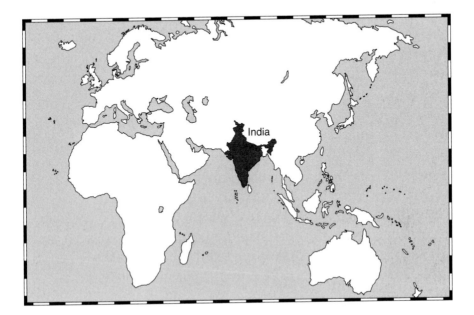

Introduction for the Teacher

Anita Desai has been writing for many years; her very popular book *A Village by the Sea* was published in 1982 and now her daughter is also a successful novelist. As Anita Desai was born and educated in India and now lives in India, Massachusetts and England, it is not surprising that the theme of her latest novel *Feasting, Fasting* is the differences between family life in the different cultures of India and America.

In this novel, which was short-listed for the 1999 Booker Prize, Uma is the eldest daughter in a conventional, contemporary middle-class Indian family. Her traditional parents are devoted but suffocating, and later in the novel they are contrasted with an American family with whom Uma's student brother lodges in Massachusetts. Whilst her brother furthers his education, the options for Uma are different. Although she wants to stay on at her convent school, her parents withdraw her from it. She is to wait at home for marriage.

[21]

The part of the story in the following extract centres on the failed attempts of Uma's parents to find their shy, young daughter a husband in the traditional way. Photographs of prospective young husbands have been sent to the family and Uma is looking at them with Aruna, her pretty younger sister.

Feasting, Fasting

It was during the sad aftermath of Anamika's marriage that all the relatives received letters from Papa to say, 'Uma is still young but may be considered of marriageable age and we see no reason to continue her studies beyond class eight –'; Papa had not informed them when Uma was withdrawn from school well before that level. The letter rippled through the ranks of the female relatives. Everywhere there was a gathering of forces. Then the ripples made their way back to the source. Some of their replies enclosed photographs of likely young men known to aunts and cousins in distant towns. Uma was shown them (a sign of the family's progressiveness). Aruna hung over her shoulder and pointed out that the tall one had spectacles and thinning hair and the fat one had bad teeth and hair that was greasy. Uma tried to shake her off, irritated by this criticism of her suitors, but she could not deny – and was rather frightened to see – that all of them bore glum, disgruntled expressions. For some reason that was not divulged to her, one of them was picked and invited to visit them along with his sister and brother-in-law who lived in the same town and even knew their neighbour, Mrs Joshi (in fact, it was she who had procured the photograph, unknown to Uma).

Mama lent one of her own saris to Uma for the occasion – a cream georgette with little sprigs of pink and blue roses embroidered all along the border. ('Old-fashioned!' sniffed Aruna. 'A granny sari!') She also did Uma's plaits up in a roll on her neck and stuck a pink flower into the roll with a long pin. 'We should powder your face a little,' she said, peering into Uma's face with an expression of dissatisfaction. 'It might cover some of the pimples. Why have you got so many pimples today? They weren't there yesterday,' she accused her.

'I get new ones all the time, Mama,' Uma said, then cried 'Ow!' as Mama rubbed some of them too hard with a flat powder puff that smelt unpleasantly of stale perspiration.

'Hold still. You have to look nice,' Mama said grimly.

'Why, Mama?' Uma squirmed, and shut her eyes as clouds of powder flew around, ferociously scented. 'It is only Joshi Aunty's friend –'

'*And* her brother from Kanpur,' Mama added significantly. 'He is in the leather business,' and she scrubbed at Uma's face as if it were a piece of hide to be offered for examination.

But it was not only leather goods that were being proffered; Uma must present other accomplishments as well. 'Now if Mrs Syal asks if *you* made the samosas, you must say *yes*.'

'Samosas!' squealed Uma, her hand flying to the most magnetic of the pimples now that Mama had stopped scrubbing at them.

'Yes, we are having samosas for tea, and barfi[1].'

'I made barfi also?'

'You *did*,' Mama threatened her with a fierce look. All this work, and nothing to show for it – that was Mama's fate. How Mama had always envied Lila Aunty for having a daughter like Anamika, a model of perfection like Anamika. No, that was not for her, she sighed.

'What if she asks me how? I won't know!' Uma cried.

'*Why* don't you know? Didn't I tell you to go to the kitchen and learn these things? For so many years I have been telling you, and did you listen? No, you were at the convent, singing those Christian hymns. You were playing games with that Anglo-Indian teacher showing you how to wear skirts and jump around. Play, play, play, that is all you ever did. Will that help you now?'

Uma would have protested if her mother had not been manhandling her quite roughly, pushing very small bangles over her large hands and onto her wrists, and even shoving her own small ruby ring onto her finger. Uma had always loved that ruby ring and tried to submit to the torture without crying, but when she looked at the swollen finger and the bluish lump caused by its tightness, she could not help worrying how she would pull it off after the tea party was over.

---

[1] barfi: Indian fudge

All through that painful afternoon, she sat trying to tear it off her finger. When her mother threw her a warning look from behind the tea tray, she stopped for a few minutes, then started again, desperately. To begin with, the visitors' attention was directed respectfully towards the mother but when it eventually came to rest, as it had to, on Uma, the girl's frantic movements could not be ignored. Finally, Mrs Syal, a large young woman who had eyed every item of Uma's clothing very closely, said, 'It is a nice ring.'

Uma, looking down at it as if it were the first time she had seen it, went red all over her face and gasped, 'My mother's.'

'Have another barfi, Mrs Syal,' said Mama, and persuaded Uma to get up and pass the plate with the sweets around again.

'Mmm, nice,' said Mrs Syal, picking up another and examining it closely. 'You made?' she asked the space just above it.

'Uma – Uma did,' Mama said, smiling ingratiatingly.

'Nice,' said Mrs Syal again, 'but my brother, he does not take sweets.'

'No? Oh, take a samosa then, take a samosa – very spicy,' cried Mama, and handed the plate of samosas to Uma to hand to the young man who sat silently and phlegmatically in a large arm chair at the other end of the room.

Uma gave up wrenching at the ring and did as she was told, and if the samosas slid and slipped all over the plate, at least none landed on the floor. She managed to cross the whole length of the room in her unaccustomed sari and offer him the samosas without an accident. Then all he did was shake his head and refuse them. He had been twisting a handkerchief in his hands throughout the party and Uma could not help noticing how dirty and ragged a piece of cloth it was. It made her look at the owner with a stir of sympathy, but when she did she could not see any sign that it was reciprocated.

The three guests left, climbing into the tonga[1] at the gate, and Mrs Syal told Mama, 'Very nice tea, very nice,' before she left, so that Mama nearly bowed in gratitude. She turned around to her

---

[1] tonga: a small horse-drawn carriage with two wheels

daughters, letting out a slow exhalation of relief. Now they could wait for the return invitation, she told them. But, unfortunately, none came, and they heard no more from the Syals. The weeks went by with decreasing hope and finally Mama relinquished it altogether, as painfully as Uma had the ring drawn from her finger. 'He must not have liked Uma,' she said bitterly, and it was not clear at whom the bitterness was directed. Then a message was brought them by their neighbour, Mrs Joshi. She pushed her way through the hedge one day, her hair streaming over her shoulders because she had washed it that morning and it was not quite dry. 'I am coming like this only,' she gasped as she climbed the steps to the veranda, placing a hand on each thigh in turn as she climbed them, 'because I must tell you – '

'The Syals sent you?' Mama cried at once, quick to pick up the tone of emergency. 'Uma, go get tea for Aunty,' she hastily ordered.

'No, no tea for me, please – it is my fast day.' Mrs Joshi sank into a basket chair and mopped her face with the end of her sari. Then she looked up, first at Mama and then at Uma. 'How can I tell you? But yesterday Mrs Syal came to see me and – you know what she said?'

'What? What?' Mama cried eagerly, swinging rapidly back and forth on the swing. When Mrs Joshi bit her tongue and held back, she worried, 'She did not like our – ?'

Mrs Joshi touched her ears to show that what she had heard had scandalized her. 'He liked – he liked – but who do you think he liked?' She leant forward and murmured into Mama's ear: 'Aruna. He wanted Mrs Syal to ask for Aruna, not Uma.'

Uma was standing behind the swing, watching and waiting, and Mrs Joshi looked up to see if she had heard. She had not, for all her efforts to do so, but at once Mama gave a scream: 'Aruna? Aruna? He asked for *her*?' and it was no use Mrs Joshi clapping her hand over her mouth and rolling her eyes towards Uma.

Uma gave a startled look and hurried away. Mama did not notice, or care. She was too scandalized, too outraged.

Anita Desai

Assignments

1 Why did Mama invite the young man and his sister and brother-in-law to tea? As she prepares Uma for the occasion, what does Mama feel are her daughter's shortcomings?

This question has two parts to it. To start with, we'll consider the first part:

Why did Mama invite the young man and his sister and brother-in-law to tea?

To answer this question, you need to read the first paragraph of the passage carefully and understand what is being planned by Uma's parents. For your answer, write a paragraph in which you refer to:

⊕ Papa's letter to the relatives
⊕ the replies received by the family
⊕ the part played by Mrs Joshi
⊕ what Mama and Papa hoped to achieve.

Now you are ready to answer the second part of the question:

As she prepares Uma for the occasion, what does Mama feel are her daughter's shortcomings?

When you are asked a question like this, you need to be careful to **select** the appropriate material to answer exactly what the question asks you. Here you need to read the passage which describes Mama getting Uma ready for the tea-party. As you read, make notes on what Mama thinks are Uma's shortcomings.
To help you, work out the answers to the following questions:
⊕ what does Mama think about Uma's face?
⊕ what is Mama's opinion of Uma's achievements at school?
⊕ what does Mama's comment about Anamika show about her opinion of Uma?

Use your notes and your answers to these questions to write a full paragraph. You have now written two full paragraphs and completed the whole question.

2 What impressions of Uma do you get from this passage?

To organize your answer, we'll divide the passage up into two parts:
⊕ the preparations
⊕ the tea party.

When you get an **impression** of Uma, you understand how she feels, how she behaves, what she looks like, all the qualities which make up a whole person.

Now, read first the part of the passage which describes Uma being prepared by her mother for the tea party. When you read this when you were doing the previous question, you were considering how Mama felt. This time you are focusing on **Uma**. As you read, write down what you learn about Uma. Sometimes the words will tell you directly, sometimes you will have to **interpret**, that is use your own ideas. It's a good idea to jot down brief quotations too.

Then, using your notes, write a paragraph on your impressions of Uma.

You could write on the first heading like this:

Uma had to put up with being dressed in a 'granny sari' and being scrubbed as she 'were a piece of hide to be offered for examination'. This makes her sound like a sacrifice, something that was going to be shown off. She seems to be very obedient and long-suffering. When her hands were made to look ugly and sore by having the ruby ring forced onto her finger, she 'tried to submit to the torture without crying'. She was suffering both physical and mental pain, but she put up with it and tried to be brave because she knew she had to.

Work through the passage in the same way for the other heading, writing up your notes into full paragraphs. You have then answered the question in full.

Second Brother's Revolt

China

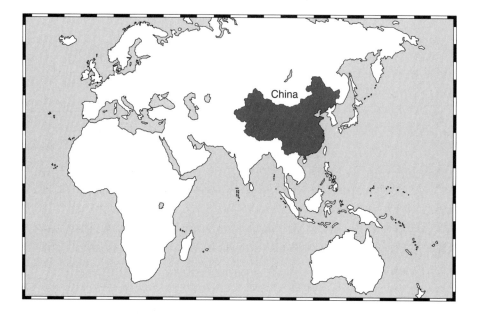

Introduction for the Teacher

Pang-Mei Natasha Chang's book tells the life story of Chang Yu-i, the author's great-aunt, who was born in 1900 in a village in Jiangsu province outside Shanghai in China. She was one of twelve children – eight boys and four girls – but her mother always said she had eight children because only the sons counted. As Chang Yu-i says: 'In China, a woman is nothing. When she is born she must obey her father. When she is married, she must obey her husband. And when she is widowed she must obey her son.'

Yu-i lived through times of tremendous change in China: in 1912 when she was twelve the last great Chinese Emperor fell and the Republic of China was established under the presidency of Dr Sun Yat-sen, and in her middle age in 1949, China's Communist state was established under Mao Zedong.

In 1903 when the incident described here took place, Chinese people still followed their ancient traditions, one of which was binding the feet of little girls so that when they grew up they would have tiny, pretty feet. In fact it meant that they would suffer a lifetime of pain and only ever be able to hobble on painful six-inch feet. The process was prolonged and excruciatingly painful, as described here. It was carried out by mothers in their unshakeable belief that the smaller a girl's feet were, the more prosperous her future husband would be. The custom was outlawed in 1902 although it was still carried out as late as the 1930's in rural parts of China where old women with bound feet can still be seen today.

Bound Feet and Western Dress

You ask me about my childhood. In China there is a legend that says that the moon used to be inhabited by two sisters. Their brother lived in the sun. The sisters, who were very beautiful, became embarrassed because people gazed at them so much during the night. They asked their brother to change homes with them. He laughed and told them that there were many more people about in the daytime than at night, so that even more eyes would be turned upward toward them. The sisters assured him that they had a plan to prevent people from looking at them. So they changed places. The two sisters went to live in the sun and their brother in the moon. Now, if a person tries to look at the sisters, the two women immediately prick at his eyes with their seventy-two embroidery needles which are the sun's rays.

That is the full legend, but there are many versions. Sometimes the tale is told as if the sisters never leave the moon, and other times the story is told as if the sisters' only home is in the sun. These are the versions of the story I heard from my amah[1] and my mama when I was little. My amah, who had grown up in the country and worked in the fields as a young girl, showed me the sisters in the moon and made me marvel at the beauty of their flowing silk robes and tiny embroidered slippers. Mama, who changed my life with one brave decision when I was three years old, taught me to imagine the sisters in the sun and to trust in the truth of things beyond sight.

My vision of the sky was filled with both pairs of sisters. At night, when my amah undressed me and combed out the braids she had plaited for me in the morning, I looked out my window for the moon sisters and fell asleep with the comfort that they

[1] amah: nursemaid

were there. Playing in the back courtyard during the day, I felt a glowlike heat at the top of my head and middle of my back and knew that the sisters in the sun were watching over me too. Because I had heard the two parts of the story separately as a child, both sides entered my heart; I saw the sisters in the sun, and I saw them in the moon.

On the twenty-third day of the twelfth lunar month of my third year, six days before the New Year Festival, my family celebrated the Little New Year called the Festival of the Kitchen God. We were not country folk but observed this custom for the servants who believed in the folklore of the gods. During the year we hung the image of the Kitchen God above the cooking stove in the kitchen, lit incense and provided fresh fruit for him every day. On the day of the festival, the Kitchen God ascended to the heavens to note for the Supreme God the virtues and vices of the household he governed. To ensure a favorable report from the Kitchen God, the servants prepared a feast in his honour and placed especially sticky glutinous rice dumplings on the shrine before his image so his lips would remain closed upon reaching the heavens.

Because these dumplings, filled with red bean paste, are mushy and tender, they are also supposed to soften the feet of little girls. It was the custom when I was little for a woman to have tiny, tiny feet. Westerners call them bound feet, but we call them something so much prettier in China: new moon or lotus petals, after the Tang Dynasty concubine who started the tradition. So beautiful a dancer was she that the Emperor had a larger-than-life lotus complete with pond constructed for her of metal and jewels, and, for his entertainment, asked her to wrap her feet in strips of silk cloth and dance among the petals of the lotus. Her graceful dance steps were like the new moon flitting among the clouds in the reflection of a lotus pond. The Emperor was so impressed that other women began to wrap their feet and bend their arches in the crescent shape of the new moon. That is how the tradition began.

How small, how beautiful, then, the bound foot. Give me your hand so you might see how it is done, how the toes of the feet are taught to curve gently around the sole of the foot until they touch your heel. Imagine your palm as the sole and your fingers as the toes. See how your fingers in your palm make a loose fist in the shape of a new moon? That is the bound foot – you end up walking on your heels and the knuckles of your toes – and if it is perfectly formed, you can slide three fingers into the niche between the toes and the heels.

My mother had three-inch feet that she had wrapped in fresh bandages every morning and bathed in perfumed water in the evening. When she walked, stiff-legged and sway-hipped, the tips of her embroidered slippers peeped out, first one and then the other, from the edge of her robe. My amah, who came from the countryside and whose feet were big like a man's, said if I was good I would grow up to be like my mother, pale and beautiful like one of the sisters in the moon. I had first seen these sisters at Moon Festival, the harvest celebration on the fifteenth day of the eighth month of the year, when the family ate round-layered pastries called mooncakes and pomegranates, which were in season. We then rose in the middle of the night to gather in the back courtyard, shivering in our nightclothes, and admire the harvest moon hanging full and heavy above us. I was two when my amah first bundled me in blankets in her arms and took me outside for the evening festivities. She told me to watch closely, to observe the swirl of mist around the moon and the faint craters in its surface. These were the signs of the sisters, she said, a hush of wonder in her voice. Then I saw them floating above me in the moon: two women in long lustrous robes and tiny silk slippers. Closing my eyes later than night, I still felt the luminous glare of the moon like a bright star in my head, and the two sisters drifted above me in my dreams.

On my third Festival of the Kitchen God, when I was three, my amah instructed me to eat an entire glutinous rice dumpling by myself. She said that it would help to soften me, but I did not know what she meant until the next morning. Mama and my amah arrived at my bedside with a basin of warm water and strips of heavy white cotton. They soaked my feet in the water and then proceeded to bind them with the thick wet bandages. When the bandages completed their first tight wraps around my feet, I saw red in front of my eyes and could not breathe. It felt as if my feet had shrunk into tiny insects. I began shrieking with pain; I thought I would die.

'What are you crying for?' my amah scolded me. 'Every little girl wants to have her feet bound.'

Mama said I would grow used to it, but that there was nothing she could do. To keep me occupied, she set up a little chair in the kitchen so that I could spend the day watching the cook prepare the meals. Only the day before, I had taken it all for granted, run across this very floor. That day, my screams filled the household as long as my strength permitted. Before lunch, my father and brothers had come by to comfort me, but as the afternoon progressed only Mama and my amah appeared in the kitchen to calm me. I could not be silenced. I watched Cook's cleaver glint up and down, heard the chicken's bones crunch beneath his blows and shrieked at the sound of it. It was as if my own toes were breaking as they curved beneath my soles.

Bound feet take years of wrapping. The toe bones have to be broken slowly, carefully. Even after a young girl's feet are perfectly formed, she has to keep them wrapped so they will stay in that shape. Prospective in-laws ask: 'Did she complain much during her foot-binding years?' If yes, then they would think twice. She was a complainer, then, not obedient enough. Even at age three, I knew. If I was good, Mama and Baba would say that my feet were perfectly formed golden lilies, that I had been even-tempered and docile during those difficult years. But if this were not true, everyone would know. The Kitchen God would tell the Supreme God. The match-maker would warn prospective families. The servants would gossip about me to other servants in the town. Everyone in Jiading knew the Chang family. If I was bad, no one would want me. I would not marry and would become a disgrace to my family. And still, I cried.

For three days I sat before my amah and Mama, enduring the ritual: the removal of bloody bandages, the soaking, the rewrapping and tightening. But on the fourth morning something miraculous happened. Second Brother, who could no longer bear my screams, told Mama to stop hurting me.

'Take the bandages off,' he said to Mama. 'It is too painful for her.'

'If I weaken now,' Mama said, 'Yu-i will suffer in the end. Who will marry her with big feet?'

Second Brother said that foot binding was a custom that was no longer beautiful.

Mama asked Second Brother again who would marry me if she let my feet alone. Second Brother then said: 'I will take care of Yu-i if no one marries her.'

Second Brother was only fifteen at the time, but he had been raised to be true to his word, and Mama relented. She called my amah over to help undo the bindings, and from that day forth I never had my feet bound again.

Shen jing bing. Crazy, my amah said about Mama's decision. Even a few years later, when the Empress Dowager passed a series of reforms banning foot binding, and Mama allowed my two younger sisters to grow their feet, my amah worried for our future. Who would marry us with big feet? We were *bu san, bu si*, neither three nor four. We could not work in the fields all day long and do the chores of a man. But neither could we just sit still and stay quiet like ladies in the female quarters.

Pang-Mei Natasha Chang

Assignments

---

1 Describe what happened to little Yu-i after she had eaten the whole rice dumpling. How did Yu-i feel about the pain she endured?

We'll start with the first part of this question:

Describe what happened to little Yu-i after she had eaten the whole rice dumpling.

Read the appropriate part of the passage. The question is asking you to **describe** what happened. You must be careful to **select** the appropriate information – don't describe parts of the passage you are not asked for. When you are describing the foot-binding ritual, don't just copy out sections of the text, but use your own words.

Now you are ready to prepare for the second part of the question:

How did Yu-i feel about the pain she endured?

Read the paragraph beginning 'Bound feet take years of wrapping' and ending 'And still, I cried' (page 32) which tells you how Yu-i felt. As you read, make notes on her different thoughts and feelings. Your notes might begin this way:

she had to be good and obedient
she had to suffer the pain so she'd have little feet
she wanted feet like lilies

Finish your notes and then you are ready to complete your answer.

Now, write two or three sentences on each point in your notes to show in detail how Yu-i felt about the pain.
The first point has been expanded for you:

Although Yu-i was only three, she had been told often enough about tiny feet to know that she had to suffer the terrible pain. Her mother gave her no choice and Yu-i knew that she had no option but to obey.

When you have written in a similar way on all the points in your notes, you have finished the whole question.

2 How does the writer associate foot binding with both pain and beauty?

This question really has three parts to it. We'll start by breaking it up. First of all, we'll look at the pain and the beauty associated with foot binding in the passage. If we look closely, we'll see that pain is associated with the reality of foot binding, and beauty with the myths surrounding it.

We'll make two headings. Read through the passage and as you read, write down appropriate sentences and phrases from the passage under each one.

Each list has been started for you.

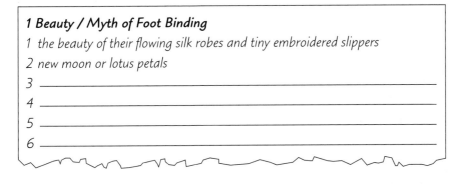

1 Beauty / Myth of Foot Binding
1 the beauty of their flowing silk robes and tiny embroidered slippers
2 new moon or lotus petals
3 _____
4 _____
5 _____
6 _____

2 Pain / Reality of Foot Binding
1 I saw red in front of my eyes
2 I began shrieking with pain; I thought I would die
3 _____
4 _____
5 _____
6 _____

When you have completed the lists, you are ready to tackle the second part of the question:

How does the writer associate foot binding with both pain and beauty?

To do this, you need to write two or three sentences on each of the examples in your list, in which you **analyse** the writer's words, that is explain how the meaning and associations of the words help to convey the beauty or the pain.

The first one from each list has been done for you:

'The beauty of their flowing silk robes and tiny embroidered slippers' describes the sisters the little girl imagined she could see in the moon. They had romantic 'flowing robes' and represented everything that was feminine and dainty. Most of all, these sisters had 'tiny' slippers, so they had tiny feet — which the little girl was taught to believe was the most beautiful and admirable thing to have.

'I saw red in front of my eyes' means that the little girl was in such terrible pain that all she could see was a wall of the colour red. Red is associated with anger, pain and blood, so it is a suitable colour. It also shows that the pain was so great that everything else was blotted out.

When you have written sentences like these for all the examples on your list, you have completed the whole question.

Child of Tibet

Tibet

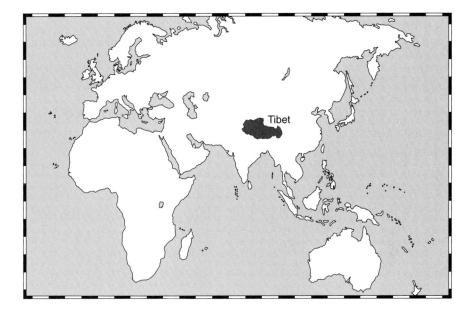

Introduction for the Teacher

A succession of Dalai Lamas have always been the spiritual leaders of Buddhist Tibet, and the writer, Jetsun Pema, is the sister of the fourteenth Dalai Lama. When a Dalai Lama dies, his reincarnation is sought in a child who was born at the time of the Dalai Lama's death. The thirteenth Dalai Lama died in 1933 and following his death, lamas and dignitaries visited the home of Jetsun Pema's parents to observe their thirteenth child, Jetsun Pema's brother, born at that auspicious time. After many tests, they were satisfied that her brother was indeed the reincarnation of the Dalai Lama of Tibet. He would be the fourteenth Dalai Lama and called His Holiness.

So, when her brother was four, the family embarked on a three-month journey to Lhasa, the capital of Tibet, where the government provided them with a 60-room house opening out onto a beautiful garden and park. This was where Jetsun Pema was born in 1940, one of nine of her parents' sixteen children to survive childhood, and this was her idyllic childhood home.

Following the Communist Chinese invasion of Tibet in 1950 which caused many thousands of deaths and enormous destruction of monasteries, the Dalai Lama was forced after 1959 to live in exile. He still lives in exile in

McCleodganj in the Indian Himalayas where he remains, as Jestun Pema says 'the spiritual beacon for those who still wait for a free Tibet'.

The passage describes Jetsun Pema's childhood memories. To Tibetans, the Tibetan name for Mother, Amala, denotes honour as well as love. Mother is the 'first lama', the first master, who teaches her children the value of compassion. This is seen in this extract which gives insights into Tibetan principles of child rearing as well as into the daily life of an unusual family.

Tibet: My Story

In spite of all they had to do, Tibetan women devoted a lot of time to their children's education, and this was so in my mother's case. When she lived in Taktser, Amala used to work in the fields, carrying a baby on her back. She always used to place him in a corner of the field, protected from sun and wind by an umbrella tied to a post stuck into the ground. That baby was His Holiness.

Until the age of five a child spends all his time with his mother. He grows up following her example. I was in fact to learn a great deal from three exceptional women: Amala, my elder sister and my aunt (my father's sister).

I now realize how essential it is that a mother always be available. Nowadays, most children do not receive all the attention they need. When they get home from school, they are often left to their own devices, because their parents work. Some people would say that children are more independent now, but is this really a good thing in the end? I personally believe that a child who is given a lot of attention will grow up happier and acquire more confidence and, later on, will in turn be able to pass on the attention and love he received.

Some readers may find my analysis a bit old-fashioned. But anyway, Tibetans allow their children to grow up gradually, remaining carefree and happy, as all children should be.

There was always someone to listen to us and take care of us in our large house. Nevertheless, when I was nearly seven, Amala thought that it was time for us to be taught outside the home.

Amala, who wanted me to receive the best possible education, did not want me to be taught with too many other pupils. My two elder brothers had been taught by a brilliant tutor, but once his task was over the government had assigned him to another region of Tibet. Amala therefore asked his assistant, a monk who had remained in Lhasa, to take charge of our education.

Up until then, my nephew and niece, our servants' three children and I had been close playmates, so my mother thought it would be best if we all received the same education. From then on we also became classmates. Our small group was joined by the son of a civil servant.

Classes started very early in the morning and, as our tutor's house was 20 minutes on horseback from our own, we had to rise before daybreak. We did not like doing this and the servants often found it hard to drag us from our beds. My nephew and niece were sometimes in such a bad mood (they were only six and four) that the servants suggested that they follow my better example. This was a way of giving me a sense of responsibility as the elder child, and today I can admit that I rather enjoyed it.

In spite of getting up so early, we were always very excited, not at the prospect of going to school, but at the thought of our daily ride. At an altitude of 10,500 feet, the mornings were pretty cold, so we would set off wrapped in blankets, after swallowing hot tea and *tsampa*[1]. I can also recall an Amdo tradition. In winter, when it is extremely cold, the wind is often very strong. Amala and my sister would prepare a mixture of milk and honey that the servants would rub onto our faces and hands. They would also cover our lips with beeswax to prevent them getting chapped; this was extremely agreeable and I loved to lick my sweet lips as I rode along.

We often arrived before our tutor, who would be kept away all morning by his important duties in the Tibetan civil service. We were welcomed by his assistant who would begin the lessons. Prayer is the first thing taught to Tibetan schoolchildren, and the first prayer they learn is dedicated to Jampal Yang, the Bodhisattva of Wisdom. As we did not yet know how to read, the monk taught it to us line by line until we were all able to recite it by heart. Then he taught us the mantra.

---

[1] tsampa: roasted flakes of barley

The lessons seemed to me to be endless. Once the recitation was over, our teacher would give us a small wooden board about one foot wide, dusted with chalk powder. He would stand behind each of us and trace horizontal lines in the chalk. Then he carefully drew the shapes of the letters of the Tibetan alphabet using a bamboo stick-pen. Placing the boards on our knees, we would then write with ink on these letters, carefully following the forms that he had made, because the slightest mistake would make us go over into the powder. This is how we learnt to write.

In fact his method became rather tedious. When the board had been completely filled, we had to wash and dry it carefully before once again dusting it with chalk powder. The assistant then drew new lines with new letters and we would copy from him over and over again. It was such painstaking work that I got blisters on my hands, and I can assure you that when you have to keep on writing the pain becomes almost unbearable. However, writing and calligraphy were so important in Tibetan schools that I managed to put up with my discomfort.

The best time of the day was at around half past ten, when a servant brought us our lunch. This servant loved opera and, every day, as soon as our little tummies began to cry out for food, we would listen out for his voice. When we heard him singing loudly in the distance, we knew that lunch was on the way.

Lunchtime was our daily break. I shared my meal, lovingly cooked by Amala, with my nephew and niece as well as with our servants' three children and the civil servant's son, who had food brought to him by another servant. My mother always said that you should share food. However, sometimes when our little companion's meal did not tempt us, we would refuse to swap dishes: something which Amala would certainly not have appreciated. The boy would look at us sadly, obviously not understanding the reason for our strange behaviour.

The afternoon was devoted entirely to reading. Unlike my nephew and niece, who managed very well, I showed little aptitude for this subject. Once our tutor arrived, he would greet us and then go off to have his lunch. As I was a bad reader, he would call me into his room and ask me to read to him throughout his meal. This was a terrible experience! As we did not have many books, he gave me religious texts to read, or else petitions addressed to the government, written on long scrolls.

Seating me opposite him, he first of all made me start with texts that were very easy. Then the texts would gradually become harder. The smell of his meal tickled my nose while I read and sometimes I even felt hungry, although I had just finished my own lunch. In vain I hoped for the moment when my tutor might offer me a mouthful of his delicious meal. Sometimes he was pleased and cut short my suffering. But as he was very strict, he often asked me to repeat sentences endlessly. The time then seemed to go by terribly slowly.

Lessons ended around three o'clock and the horses were then brought round so that we could return home, where we would gobble up the delicious meal Amala had cooked for us.

Throughout their schooling, Tibetan children are given very little homework so, once our meal was over, we were once again free to play.

Jetsun Pema

Assignments

1 What did Jetsun Pema like and dislike about her school day?

To make your answer detailed and clearly organized, we'll break the school day up into distinct parts:
- the journey to school
- learning to write
- reading to the Tutor
- showing the Tutor the writing boards.

Read each part of the passage and as you read, make notes under each heading in two columns, a 'like' column and a 'dislike' column. When you have finished, use your notes to write a paragraph on each heading making clear what Jetsun liked and disliked.

The first one has been written for you:

> *Jetsun Pema did not like having to get up before daybreak to be ready for the journey, but she enjoyed the responsibility of making her young nephew and niece get up. Although the high altitude in Tibet meant that it was very cold, she was excited by the horse ride to school. She liked licking the sweet beeswax from her lips which, along with the honey and milk on her face and hands, was put on to protect her from the fierce wind.*

When you have completed all four, you have completed your answer to the question.

2 The following four sentences from the passage express Tibetan ideas on child-rearing:

   a *In spite of all they had to do, Tibetan women devoted a lot of time to their children's education, and this was so in my mother's case.*

   b *Tibetans allow their children to grow up gradually, remaining carefree and happy, as all children should be.*

   c *Up until then, my nephew and niece, our servants' three children and I had been close playmates, so my mother thought it would be best if we all received the same education.*

   d *I shared my meal, lovingly cooked by Amala, with my nephew and niece as well as with our servants' three children; my mother always said you should share food.*

   Explain the Tibetan ideas on child-rearing expressed. How do the words used suggest Jetsun Pema's feelings and attitude?

Each sentence in the box tells you something about what the Tibetan ideas on bringing up children were. There is a lot to read all at once, so we'll take it sentence by sentence. Read the first one carefully. The task is:

   Explain the Tibetan ideas on child-rearing expressed.

This first sentence tells you something about the importance of women in the Tibetan family. Explain in a few sentences what you think the sentence is telling you about this topic.

Now you are ready to answer the second part of the question:

How do the words used suggest Jetsun Pema's attitude?

To prepare for this second part, you need to look closely at the writer's words in the sentence. There is at least one word which is 'coloured' by the writer's attitude.

In this first sentence the 'coloured' word is: **devoted**.

If the writer had used a neutral word like 'gave', it would not suggest her attitude in the way that 'devoted' does.

Now, you need to explain what the 'coloured' word tells you about Jetsun's attitude. This first one has been explained for you:

'Devoted' suggests that the Tibetan mother gave a great deal of time to their children's education and Jetsun Pema thinks that it is a good idea to do so. The word is like 'devotion' and so Jetsun Pema makes it sound as though she felt it was a loving thing to do and the mother was right to think it was very important to spend time on the children's education.

Now, work through the other three sentences, writing answers in the same way.

To help you, here are the topics for each sentence:
⊕ sentence b: making childhood a time for happiness
⊕ sentence c: giving children educational opportunities
⊕ sentence d: how to treat others.

When you have completed your writing on each sentence, you have completed the whole question.

Stranded

Netherlands

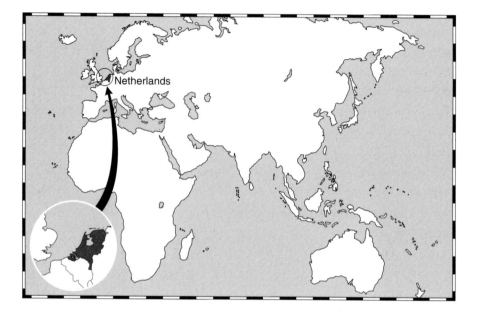

Netherlands

Introduction for the Teacher

Edith Velmans and her brother were happy teenagers living with loving Jewish parents in Holland, when the Nazi invasion of their country in 1940 changed the life of the family for ever. More and more anti-Jewish laws came into effect and Edith could no longer go to school. As life became even more dangerous for Jews, she was sent away to another town, Breda, to live under an assumed identity with a non-Jewish family who risked their lives in sheltering her. In her new family, she grew to love her 'Aunt Tine', and Ineke became a sister to her.

Edith wrote many letters to her parents and brother, all of whom were to die during the war years that followed, and, like Anne Frank, she kept a diary. Although, like Anne Frank again, her mother and brother died in concentration camps, Edith survived. It was not until 1998 that she published her account of the war years based on those letters and diaries. It makes a heartening postscript to the story to learn that Aunt Tine, Edith's beloved second 'mother', lived to the age of 100. She died in 1994.

In this chapter from the book, Edith and Ineke find themselves in very real danger. Edith has been to make a secret and rare visit to her sick father and she and Ineke are returning home to Breda, but find themselves on the wrong train. It will not stop at Breda and they will not be able to get a train back before the 8pm curfew. If Edith is found on the streets, her false identity will be found out and she and the family will be arrested.

Edith's Book

After visiting Father, there was nothing to do but return to Breda. Ineke and I had arranged to meet under the central clock at the train station. As I made my way through the crowds, I was jostled by a group of young German soldiers hurrying past. I felt the rough wool of their uniforms rub against my arm, and gazed straight ahead. I started noticing the people milling about, wondering if any of them were, like me, not who they were supposed to be. Or was I the only one? The only thing you could be sure of was that some of them were Nazi sympathizers – they would turn you in, given half a chance. But how could you tell which was which – who was good and who was bad?

To my great relief, there, under the clock, surrounded by shivering travellers, was Ineke, her calm pale eyes searching for me. My 'sister'. We fell on each other like long-lost friends. With Ineke at my side, I felt inconspicuous, safe. Two giggly girls on an outing. We found a compartment which was freezing cold, but empty. 'They'll turn on the heat once the train starts moving,' we told each other hopefully.

After two days, there was so much to tell. I filled Ineke in about my visit to Father, and I had just started telling her about 'Alfred' when three men in business suits entered our compartment, blowing into their cupped hands to warm their freezing fingers. They sat down without saying a word. Soon two of them were absorbed in their newspapers; the third sat staring out of the window with a tired, empty gaze and then nodded off. We kept our voices down, careful not to say anything that could give us away. We were both shivering, and huddled close to each other for warmth: the heat never came on.

After the second stop, as the train slowly moved out of the station, I noticed the sign 'Philips Gloeilampen Fabriek' (Philips Light Bulb Factory). I wondered out loud why we had not seen the

Philips factory on our way out. 'Maybe we were talking so much that we just didn't notice it,' said Ineke.

Then I jumped out of my seat. 'Philips! Philips is in Eindhoven!' Eindhoven was due east of Breda. Anxiously we looked at our travelling companions. 'Is this the train for Breda?' we asked.

'No, you are on your way to Maastrict, I'm afraid,' said one of them, shaking his head. 'You should have changed trains at the first stop.'

The train was now moving at top speed. It was too late to get off. On the way to Utrecht we had been on the express train, and no one had informed us that we'd have to change trains on the return journey. 'There is only one thing to do,' the businessman said. 'You'll have to get off at the next stop, Weert, and take the first train back.'

It was six p.m. and it was getting dark. Anxiously we asked the conductor what to do, and he informed us, shaking his head, that our train would arrive in Weert too late to make the connection back to Utrecht that night, since all rail traffic stopped after the eight p.m. general curfew. We looked at each other in horror. What to do? We would have to be off the streets from eight until six the next morning. We didn't know a soul in Weert.

Ineke patted my hand as we tried to hide our consternation from our fellow passengers. My mind was racing, but I told myself to remain calm. In silence, we stared out at the dusky meadows racing by with dark clusters of cows huddled together against the cold. Now and then we would catch each other's eyes in the reflection in the window.

I went over the options, one by one. No good going to the police for help, of course. The same went for a hotel or inn: at the reception desk, we would be asked to show our identity papers. More likely than not these would then be taken to the police station or Gestapo headquarters to be checked. Every person who stayed away from his place of residence for longer than twenty-four hours was supposed to register with the police in the town he or she was visiting. I knew the Germans had a registry of lost or stolen identity cards – it was easy for them to catch 'illegals' like myself.

By the time we got off the train, we had less than an hour to find a solution. Who would take us in? We did not have enough money to bribe someone; besides, how would we know whom to trust?

Walking from the station into the centre of town, we quickly decided on a story. Two sisters, from a poor family, we were on our way back from visiting our grandfather in Utrecht but we boarded the wrong train and now found ourselves stranded with no money for a hotel. 'But where shall we go?' moaned Ineke.

An inspiration came to me. 'A doctor or a priest. Human lives are important to them. If we can't trust one of them, we can't trust anyone.' Ineke thought that this was a good idea. It was now 7.30, half an hour until curfew.

We found ourselves on a quiet street. The houses were all dark, because of the blackout. We imagined families safely gathered round the dinner table behind their heavy curtains or black blinds, eating their supper by lamplight and the shimmering of a Christmas tree. A young woman was hurrying towards us carrying a child on her hip. We decided we'd risk it. After all, she looked sympathetic and she had a child. How could she be bad? 'Excuse us,' we asked politely, 'but could you please tell us where we could find a doctor or a priest?' Hurriedly we told her the story we'd made up. 'So you see,' we said, 'we have to get off the street somehow. We were hoping to find someone who would let us into their garden or shed, just for tonight.'

'You're in luck, girls,' the young woman said. 'You happen to be standing right in front of the vicarage. Father Josephus lives here. Try him!' Then she hurried on, explaining she'd be late for curfew.

The vicarage was a tall, white, elegant old townhouse. There was not a chink of light to show if anyone was home. We pulled the heavy brass bell by the side of the door. We waited a long time. We heard no sound inside. We rang the bell again, more urgently this time. I was beginning to lose hope.

Then, suddenly, we heard a scratching at the doorknob. I thought my heart would be crushed in my chest, it was beating so hard. This was perhaps the scariest moment of my life – but it was also exciting. My life had suddenly turned into an adventure!

An old woman opened the door. After we stammered out our

story, she opened the door all the way and told us to enter. 'Wait in the hall,' she said, 'and I'll tell Pater Josephus that he has visitors.' After a long miserable wait, a middle-aged man in a dressing-gown and slippers came down the stairs. I decided he had a kind and open face. He acted as if our plea to be allowed to spend the night in his garden or shed was the most normal request in the world.

'No, no,' he said, 'just come in! You don't have to stay out in the garden. Here, come into the parlour, where it's nice and warm. Pull a chair up to the fire and relax.' He told his housekeeper to bring us some food, which we fell on ravenously. Then he sat with us a while, talking about literature, philosophy and other neutral subjects. He never once asked us a personal question about ourselves.

Eventually he excused himself, but not before making sure that his housekeeper had brought us everything we needed for the night – pillows, blankets and a footstool, so that we could rest comfortably in our chairs by the fire. We fell asleep at once, grateful to be indoors, out of the dark January night.

At five a.m. the housekeeper woke us with a cup of hot coffee (made with real coffee beans!), farmer's bread, fresh butter and home-made jam. We splashed some cold water on our faces, then ate our delicious breakfast and thanked our host profusely. Father Josephus walked us to the door and handed us a package containing fresh bacon, butter, eggs and a loaf of bread hot from the oven. 'For your parents,' he said. 'Because they must have had a pretty unpleasant night, not knowing where you were. Please don't thank me. Just catch your train and get home safe, do you hear? God bless you, girls.'

After the war I sent a letter with a little gift to Pater Josephus in the town of Weert, thanking him for saving my life. The package come back stamped 'Addressee unknown'. I tried to find out what had happened to him, but no one could tell me where he had gone. Much later I discovered that Pater Josephus had been in the Resistance and, like many other priests, had been caught and executed.

Edith Velmans

Assignments

1 What kind of man is Pater Josephus?

This is certainly a short question – but you need to write a full answer!

The writer relates the words and actions of Pater Josephus, but she does not tell you exactly what sort of man he was. To answer this question, **you** need to interpret his words and actions and explain what sort of man you think he was.

So, first of all, read the extract and as you read, make a list of what Pater Josephus said and did. The first one has been done for you.

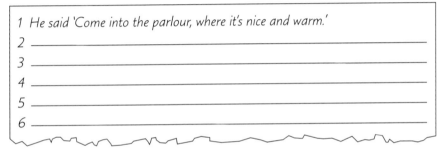

1 He said 'Come into the parlour, where it's nice and warm.'

2 _____

3 _____

4 _____

5 _____

6 _____

The next step is to go through each example on your list and **interpret** it, that is you decide from the evidence what sort of man Pater Josephus was.

To do this, you will need to add a sentence or two to explain what you think.

The first one has been completed for you:

He said 'Come into the parlour, where it's nice and warm.'
This shows that Pater Jospehus is kind and welcoming and anxious to help the girls. He is understanding because he knows straight away the girls are in trouble.

When you have finished going through your list like this, you will have your answer to the question.

2 How does the writer convey the girls' different feelings in this chapter?

This question really has two parts:

   1 what are the girls' different feelings?
   2 how does the writer **convey**, that is **show**, these feelings?

First of all, read through the passage again carefully. As you read, make a list of the feelings which the girls experience.
Your list could start like this:

> 1 *Edith felt threatened*
> 2 *they were very cold*
> 3 _____
> 4 _____
> 5 _____
> 6 _____

Having worked out the girls' feelings, you now need to cover the second part of the question:

   How does the writer convey the feelings?

To do this, you need to use details from the text. Looking at the effect of particular words and punctuation will help you.
Take each of the feelings on your list and write a paragraph in which you use details from the text to show **how** the writer conveys these feelings to you.
The first paragraph has been done for you:

> *Edith feels very threatened when she is alone walking towards the station clock where she is to meet Ineke. The German soldiers she goes past seem threatening because she feels their uniforms brush against her as though they were attracting her attention. She feels so guilty about hiding her identity that she wonders if others are hiding the same secret. The questions she asks herself, 'who was good and who was bad?' shows that she is confused. The two dashes used in two sentences show that her thoughts are spinning.*

When you have written your paragraphs for all the feelings on your list in this way, you have answered the question.

Eggless
China and Hong Kong

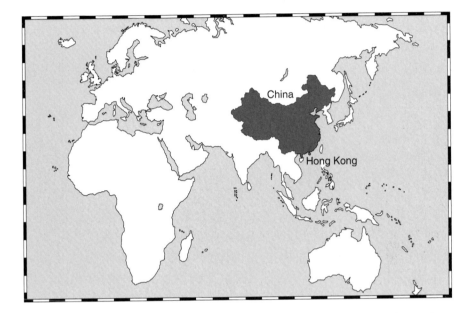

Introduction for the Teacher

During Adeline Yen Mah's childhood, China was racked by wars and upheaval. Adeline was born in Tianjin in 1937, at the beginning of the Sino-Japanese War which was to last for the first eight years of her life. By the time she was eleven and attending the boarding school where she spent every single day of the year, another war was raging in China. Tianjin was filling with desperate and sick refugees from the civil war between the nationalists and the communists, and the school dwindled to one mixed class of 7–17 year olds as parents took their children away to safety.

Unclaimed by her father and stepmother, Adeline remained. Finally her aunt rescued her and the family fled to the safety of the British crown colony of Hong Kong. (The island of Hong Kong had been ceded to Britain by China after the First Opium War of 1842, and the so-called New Territories later in the nineteenth century. Both were finally returned to China in 1997). It was in Hong Kong that in 1949 Adeline was enrolled at The Sacred Heart, a Catholic boarding school which accepted boarders and orphans.

All the political commotion, however, was nothing to Adeline in comparison with the cruel, miserable daily life she had to endure at home. Her mother

[51]

had died two weeks after giving birth to her and Adeline was never even shown a photograph of her. Her father quickly remarried an exceptionally unkind woman and had more children. As an unwanted daughter, Adeline was treated with unrelenting harshness. This extract describes her life as a twelve-year-old at the boarding school in Hong Kong. She was deeply relieved to be enrolled as a boarder and not as an orphan, since as an orphan, she would have been used as a domestic servant, or even sold as a child slave.

Falling Leaves

When I was enrolled there were sixty-six boarders. Throughout my years there, I never entirely overcame the very real fear of being transferred to the orphanage section. I would then cost my Father nothing.

On admission as boarder, each child was assigned an identification number. From then on, all our belongings were stamped with that number. Our day started at five forty-five. A loud bell aroused us from bed. Daily mass was compulsory. My friend Mary Suen, who was not an early riser, used to complain that it was 'just like being a nun, whether you wish to be holy or not.' The only legitimate excuse for escaping mass was serious illness, pretended or otherwise. All through mass most of us would have just one thought: getting out of the chapel as soon as possible and rushing into the dining-room for breakfast. Seating was prearranged and could not be altered; they placed us according to our age. Mary sat to my immediate left.

We were each given a pigeonhole in a huge cupboard prominently displayed in the dining-room. Each boarder would store her provisions from home in her allotted space, duly numbered. The abundance or scantiness of your very own food supply was readily visible to all the girls. It was a barometer of the degree of affection accorded to you by your family. During my entire stay at Sacred Heart, my pigeonhole was perpetually empty.

Eggs had special significance. They had to be brought from home and were stored in the refrigerator in the kitchen. Before handing them over, each boarder was required to paint her number in indelible ink on the shells.

For breakfast we each had two slices of bread, a pat of butter and a portion of jam. For those lucky ones whose parents paid an extra fifteen dollars per month, there was hot milk into which you could stir your own supply of chocolate or Ovaltine from your pigeonhole. Some girls brought out anchovy paste, Marmite, chicken liven pâté or canned tuna to spread on their bread. Mother Mary would then bring in a huge vat of piping hot, freshly boiled eggs. She used to pick up the eggs one by one and place them in individual egg cups, reading out the numbers as she worked. You walked up to her when you heard your number and retrieved your egg.

Those eggs became symbols of rare privilege. They were cheap and readily available in the markets, but having your number called by Mother Mary meant that someone from home loved you enough to bring you eggs so that you would eat a nourishing breakfast. Just because your family was rich did not mean that you automatically received an egg. You could not charge eggs to your account like milk or piano lessons. The breakfast egg, more than anything, divided us into two distinct and transparent groups: the loved ones and the unloved ones. Needless to say, I remained eggless throughout my tenure at Sacred Heart.

After breakfast, we rushed to pick up our books from the study room and join the day girls in the playground. Classes started at eight. Lessons were in English but we spoke to each other in Cantonese. To my surprise, the months I had spent at St Joseph's[1] had given me sufficient grounding to keep up with my studies.

At noon, the school broke for lunch. We boarders were summoned by a bell into the dining-room. There we found a plate of spaghetti and meat balls, or macaroni and cheese. On good days, we were served pork chops and rice, and sautéd vegetables with mashed potatoes. 'So called western food!' Mary muttered under her breath. 'Give me a bowl of wonton soup[2] any day.'

Afternoon school was from one thirty to three thirty. Tea was served in the dining-room at four. It was the only meal you were

---

[1] St Joseph's: Adeline's previous school
[2] wonton soup: meat dumpling soup

free to partake of or not. This was the hour when the haves could really show off to the have-nots. Besides the usual bread, butter and jam, out came the goodies brought in during Sunday's visiting hours: chocolates, biscuits, candies, beef jerky[3], preserved fruits, assorted nuts. On birthdays, the birthday girl was allowed to change out of her uniform into a pretty dress. Decked out in dainty lace, ribbons and bows she dispensed largesse to the rest of us while parading next to Mother Mary behind an enormous birthday cake ablaze with the appropriate number of candles. We sang 'Happy Birthday'. The cake was sliced and arranged on a platter. Mother Mary and the birthday girl then went around the room from boarder to boarder, serving or withholding a piece of cake as she wished. After this little game of discrimination, the birthday girl would open her presents while we oohed and aahed over them.

My habit was to go to tea a little later, wolf down my bread, butter and jam as fast as possible, then bolt out of the door. I knew that there would never be a birthday celebration for me. At no time could I ever reciprocate in kind or buy anyone a birthday present. My friend Mary and I did not speak to each other about any of this, but I often found some treats from her laid out on my plate: a few coconut candies, a packet of preserved plums, a piece of fruit.

Mary was not considered academically clever. She had difficulty with maths and often asked me for help. She used to sit by my side as I worked on her assignments, saying, 'It's so obvious now. Why didn't *I* think of it?' I would bask in her admiration and try even harder.

In other ways Mary was wise beyond her years. When Daisy Chen was first admitted as a boarder, I noted that she had a Shanghai accent and was curious about her background. I must have asked a few too many questions. Daisy became vague and evasive. Afterwards Mary said to me, 'Don't ask such questions. Girls like us who end up here usually come from unhappy homes. It's better not to ask. Her story'll come out in the end anyway.' I kicked myself for being insensitive and boorish.

---

[3] beef jerky: preserved strips of beef`

After tea, there was an hour of recreation. We were free to play with our dolls, read novels, skip rope, practise the piano, roller skate, compete in softball or shoot a few baskets. I usually visited the library.

It was a large square room tucked away in one corner of the boards' wing. Its floor-to-ceiling shelves were lined with books. Most of them were in English. A few were in Italian or Latin. There were no Chinese books.

Oh, what magic it held for me to walk into this treasure trove where the written word was king! The windows were small. The lights were dim. Because of this, the room was dark and forbidding. There was no librarian. Many of the volumes were reference books or magazines which could not be removed. The rest was a kaleidoscope of every subject under the sun. We were allowed to check out as many books as we wished. Mother Louisa was in charge and locked the doors promptly at five. Since tea was from four to five, I was usually the only one there. Often I encountered Mother Louisa on my way out, my arms loaded with the latest batch of reading material. I became such a familiar sight that she often looked out for me before locking up. 'Is the "scholar" out of her lair?' she would joke, jangling her keys. 'Or is she spending the night in here?'

She gave me that nickname because a maths problem I had helped Mary solve proved to be more correct than the one in her textbook. It was probably just a printing error but the story made the rounds and reached the other boarders. Many came to me when they had problems with their homework.

They started to overlook my one and only Sunday dress which was too short, too tight and too small for me, my worn shoes with holes in the soles, my empty pigeonhole and even my egglessness.

Adeline Yen Mah

Assignments

1 In what ways did her friendship with Mary affect Adeline? How did Adeline's intelligence make life at school easier for her?

There are two parts to this question. To answer them in detail, you'll need to select words and phrases from the passage and add your own ideas.
We'll start by answering the first part:

In what ways did her friendship with Mary affect Adeline?

As you read the passage about Mary (page 54), write notes on the following questions, answering them in your own words. It's a good idea to quote words and phrases from the passage as well, but use brief quotations. Always write a comment which explains your quotations, don't just copy bits out without comment.

- how did Adeline feel when she found Mary's treats on her plate?
- what difference did helping Mary with her maths make to Adeline?
- what did Adeline feel about Mary's comments on Daisy Chen?

Now you are ready to consider the second part of the question:

How did Adeline's intelligence make life at school easier for her?

Read the rest of the extract (from 'After tea, there was an hour of recreation' to the end) and write notes on the following questions as you did for the ones above:

- in which two ways did the library make school life easier for Adeline?
- what were the consequences for Adeline of her helping the girls with their homework?

Now you can use the evidence and explanations you have collected on each bullet point question to write a paragraph for each one.

You now have five paragraphs and have completed the question.

2 How does the writer convey the significance of food in this passage?

This question also has two parts and is really asking you to do two things:
1 **identify** the different kinds of food
2 **explain** the **significance** of the food.

As you read the passage, write down all the different kinds of food:

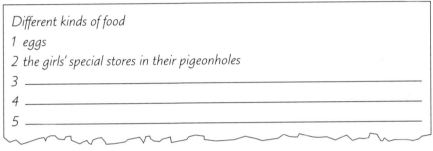

Different kinds of food
1 eggs
2 the girls' special stores in their pigeonholes
3 _____
4 _____
5 _____

When you have completed the list, you are ready for the more difficult part: **explain** the **significance** of the food.
The writer describes all the different kinds of food on your list partly because that was what the girls ate. But most of all, the food for this poor abandoned little girl is important for another reason. It means, or **symbolizes**, something else for her. This is the **significance** asked for in the question.
Think carefully about it, and explain in a paragraph the significance of each of the foods on your list.
The first paragraph has been done for you:

Eggs had a 'special significance'. This meant that eggs were particularly symbolic. They meant that someone at home loved the girl enough to care whether she had a good breakfast. They symbolized the parents' love. They were a 'rare privilege' which meant that the girls were especially lucky to have them. The presence or absence of eggs made two 'transparent' groups. The girls who had eggs could see very clearly which girls didn't have eggs. They could see that no-one at home loved the girls who didn't have eggs.

When you have written paragraphs on all the different foods on your list in this way, you have answered the whole question.

Storm at Sea
Japan

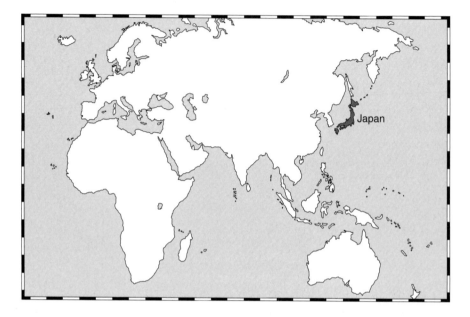

Introduction for the Teacher

This story of *Storm at Sea* takes place in the 1930's when a hugely powerful Emperor still ruled over the Japanese Empire.

Hideto is a sixteen-year-old boy at boarding school at this time. He had been in trouble at school but his father Tei-ichi, a much respected doctor, would not punish him again. He said the school had already punished him. But then Hideto became involved in something much more serious: a school strike. An idealistic young master had encouraged the boys to strike and, although Hideto was not the ringleader, his offence was considered very serious indeed because of the mood of the times. Twelve people had just been executed for plotting to assassinate the Emperor; any kind of anti-imperialism or anti-militarism was severely punished. The Military Police were increasing their influence and any kind of rebellion was dangerous.

Hideto should have been expelled, but his mother, Kei, apologized to the teachers and Hideto was allowed to stay. Kei did not lose faith in her son, but understood his foolishness. 'Only those who are stupid never get into trouble when they are young,' she said, 'but only stupid ones go on being trouble after they grow up.'

During the summer holidays that followed, Hideto's older brother, Yasuharu, returned from university where he was training to be a doctor and brought a friend, Dr Komoto, with him. They went out on a fishing trip, together with the boys' young nephew Shuichi. On that fishing trip, something happened which proved that Kei was right not to have lost faith in her younger son.

Information for the Reader

Because the people's names in this story could be confusing when you first read it, here they are:

Dr Komoto – Yasuharu's university friend
Hideto – 16-year-old brother
Kei – the brothers' mother
Matabei (Mata) – trusted house-servant
Shige – cook
Shuichi (Shu-chan) – the brothers' 8-year-old nephew
Tei-ichi – the brothers' father
Yasuharu (Yasu) – 18-year-old brother

Fish of the Seto Inland Sea

The summer holiday came and Yasuharu returned home. He brought with him a friend who was a paediatrician[1]. The children were told to call him Dr Komoto but, in spite of the formal address, he was soon joining in with wrestling, games and other lively activities.

The days passed, happy and uneventful, until the day that Yasuharu, Dr Komoto, Hideto and Shuichi decided to go sea fishing. Early in the morning, they left, both Yasuharu and Dr Komoto in *yukata*, cotton kimono, and Hideto and Shuichi in cotton shorts, all wearing straw hats. The day promised to be fine. They carried rice balls that Shige had made. The rice balls had cooked seaweed inside instead of the usual pickled plums. Pickled plums prevented the rice from going sour but, if taken fishing, Shige insisted, there would not be any catch.

'Oh? That won't do, Shige san[2]. Thank you,' Dr Komoto said politely. Yasuharu just opened his mouth and laughed noiselessly.

---

[1] paediatrician: doctor who specializes in treating children
[2] san: term of respect, like Mrs

At the shore, a fisherman was waiting for them with a small boat. He said, 'It is windy further offshore. Come home early before the weather changes.' But the sky was deep blue and the temperature was rising. The sun was already strong. They got into the boat and the fisherman pushed it out into the water.

'Shu-chan, you must get as tanned and strong as Hideto,' Yasuharu said. Yasuharu, Dr Komoto and Hideto rowed the boat in turn until they were a long way from the shore. They were all happily fishing when Dr Komoto said, 'Oh?' and looked up at the sky.

The wind was getting cool and he thought he felt a raindrop on his face. But he did not pay further attention as Yasuharu and Hideto did not seem to be worried. They were brought up in the area, he thought, they should know. But although they had grown up near the sea, neither Yasuharu nor Hideto had much knowledge or experience of boats. Yasuharu looked up at the sky as large drops of rain started to come down on them.

'It will pass,' he said, and asked Shuichi if he was cold. Shuichi was catching the rain water running down his cheeks by sticking out a lower lip. He shook his head. The boat began to sway and he was a little afraid but he trusted his uncles and was quietly holding on to the side of the boat.

As the wind rose, wave after wave crashed into the small boat.

'Hideto, scoop up the water in the boat with your hat,' Yasuharu said and Dr Komoto and Hideto started to bail out water.

'Shu-chan, you help us, too,' Hideto said and Shuichi joined them. The boat was lifted up by a big wave and crashed down and reeled round. Despite all their efforts, they were soon ankle-deep in water.

'Shu-chan, come here,' Yasuharu said, and pulled him to his side.

'Which way is the wind coming from?' Dr Komoto said. In the middle of the storm, Hideto thought the question was silly and inconsequential, but then it occurred to him that Dr Komoto might be trying to compose himself.

'It seems to be blowing us along the shore,' he answered.

At home, the three girls were sitting around Kei sewing doll's clothes. The pieces of cloth the girls were given were mostly dark-coloured cotton with stripes. Silk remnants were kept to make cushions for guests or sleeveless tops, but Kei gave them each a small piece of brightly coloured, patterned silk. The material was carefully smoothed with a flat-iron. Kei had taken it out from a chest of drawers with large iron handles.

As they all bent down around Kei's sewing box, Tei-ichi said from the veranda, 'Has Yasu not come home yet?'

'No, he has not come home,' Kei said.

Tei-ichi's voice was heard calling Matabei. The girls had not noticed but the raindrops were causing ripples on the surface of the pond. Plantain leaves swayed and rustled. Kei said, 'You stay here,' to the girls and hurried to join Tei-ichi.

Matabei ran out barefoot into the rain towards the sea wearing a waterproof cape.

'Yasuharu is with them. They will be all right,' Tei-ichi said, and went back to his study. The rain was getting harder.

The girls felt restless and put away their sewing. Shige came into the kitchen and started to make a fire in the range. The dark and damp kitchen became steamy and hot. Shige said, 'Don't worry. Mata will soon bring them back.'

While it was getting dark inside the house, it was not yet dark on the sea, but the rain was coming down harder and the bottom of the boat was full of water. The straw hats were no longer useful. Many times the boat nearly capsized and Yasuharu realized that it would soon start to sink.

'Hideto,' Yasuharu called. 'You are the best swimmer in the prefecture, aren't you?'

Hideto said, 'Yes,' but the sea around them was so different from the sea on the day of the swimming competition.

'Hideto,' Yasuharu called again, keeping his balance. 'Carry Shuichi on your back and swim back to the shore.'

Hideto could not believe what he was hearing. It was true he was the best swimmer in the prefecture. For two years he had come first at the all prefecture swimming competitions for the adults. He had never felt tired, even after swimming a long-distance race. He remembered the sight of many heads behind him all in a line as though they were strung together by a long string, and the roll of drums from boats with flags bobbing up and down. The sky was blue and there were spectacular summer clouds. There was also sweet crystallized sugar thrust from the boats in a long-handled spoon.

Hideto was about to say, 'I cannot do it. It is not possible,' when his brother ordered him with all the authority of an eldest brother. 'Don't think. Just do it. We have to save Shu-chan... Look there!' Yasuharu had seen the faint glimmer of lights.

Yasuharu untied his sash and passed it across the little boy's goose-pimpled back, under his arms and around Hideto's chest. He crossed it in front, wound it back and tied it securely.

'Go!' Hideto jumped into the water. Even though he was the best swimmer in the prefecture, for the sixteen-year-old, an eight-year-old boy was heavy. Tossed about by the waves Hideto swam. Shuichi was holding on to him tightly.

At the shore, a big fire had been built. Women and children were out, and as the children ran near the fire, mothers and grandmothers scolded them. Men were calling, 'Shuichi dansama[1], Yasuharu dansama, Hideto dansama, Doctor Komoto,' in turn.

Hideto appeared, staggering in the light of the torches, supported by a group of men who had formed a search party down the coast. One of them carried Shuichi.

Yasuharu and Dr Komoto arrived a few minutes later. They had abandoned the sinking boat shortly after Hideto.

Hideto was sitting in front of the fire, hugging his knees. Kei stroked his back. She was saying, 'Oh, well done. You are brave. Well done,' with a tear-stained face.

They could not find Tei-ichi. Only Matabei knew where he was.

---

[1] dansama: term of respect, like 'Master'

He was standing alone on a cliff overlooking the sea, but Matabei did not tell anyone.

The next day, Tei-ichi called Hideto. He said, 'I will give this to you,' and gave him an antique sword forged by a famous swordsmith. It was the most precious treasure belonging to the family.

Ruri Pilgrim

Assignments

---

1 In the story, trust is placed in different people. How trustworthy do they turn out to be?

To make your answer structured and organized, we'll take from the passage three examples of trust being placed in different people:
1 Dr Komoto's trust in Yasuharu and Hideto's boating experience
2 Yasuharu's trust in his brother Hideto's strength in swimming
3 the trust placed in the house servant, Matabei.

You are going to focus on these three examples, so write them down as headings. Read the passage carefully and make notes under each heading as you go.
When you have finished reading, write the answers to the following questions underneath your notes. You will probably have to go back to the passage. The answers won't always be obvious, you will have to think about and **interpret** what is going on in the story.

Dr Komoto's trust in Yasuharu and Hideto's boating experience
- why didn't Dr Komoto take much notice of the warning drops of rain?
- what was Yasuharu's reaction to the large drops of rain?
- how well did the brothers look after Dr Komoto?

Yasuharu's trust in his brother Hideto's strength in swimming
- what did Yasuharu entrust to Hideto?
- why was Hideto unsure if he was worthy of that trust?
- how successful was he in carrying out what his brother demanded of him?
- why did Hideto's father give him the sword?

The trust placed in the house servant, Matabei
- what did Shige trust Matabei to do?
- what information did Matabei keep to himself?
- how deserving was Matabei of the trust placed in him?

Now, using your notes and the answers you have written to these questions, write a full paragraph on each heading explaining how trustworthy the people were.

2 Write in as much detail as you can on the interpretation of the following lines from the passage:

  a *The rice balls had cooked seaweed inside instead of the usual pickled plums. Pickled plums prevented the rice from going sour but, if taken fishing, Shige insisted, there would be no catch.*
   'Oh? That won't do, Shige san. Thank you,' Dr Komoto said politely. Yasuharu just opened his mouth and laughed noiselessly.
  b *The girls had not noticed but the raindrops were causing ripples on the surface of the pond. Plantain leaves swayed and rustled. Kei said, 'You stay here,' to the girls and hurried to join Tei-ichi.*
   Matabei ran out barefoot into the rain towards the sea wearing a waterproof cape.
  c *He remembered the sight of many heads behind him all in a line as though they were strung together by a long string, and the roll of drums from boats with flags bobbing up and down. The sky was blue and there were spectacular summer clouds. There was also sweet crystallized sugar thrust from the boats in a long-handled spoon.*
  d *The next day, Tei-ichi called Hideto. He said, 'I will give this to you,' and gave him an antique sword forged by a famous swordsmith. It was the most precious treasure belonging to the family.*

This is much less complicated than it looks!

First of all, read the passage, and then turn to the first extract in the question box. The question asks you to **interpret** the four extracts from the passage. This means that as well as understanding what the extract is about, you also need to explain its **significance**. You need to question the words used and ask yourself **why** they have been used.

For example, in the first extract, you need to ask yourself questions like:

⊕ why did Shige say there'd be no catch if they took plum rice balls?
⊕ why had she gone to so much trouble to prepare the boys' food?
⊕ in what tone of voice did Dr Komoto say 'That won't do'?
⊕ why did Yasuharu laugh 'noiselessly'?

In this way, you will discover meanings and significance – you will be **interpreting**.

You would then be able to write an answer to the first extract like:

> Shige is obviously very fond of the family she helps to look after and wants their fishing expedition to be successful. She is not educated like Dr Komoto and Yasuharu, and is deeply superstitious. She believes that the traditional pickled plums would prevent them from catching any fish, so she has put seaweed in the rice balls instead. Dr Komoto doesn't believe the superstition, but appreciates her kindness and answers politely as a guest should do. Yasuharu, who is used to Shige's superstitions, just laughs, but noiselessly so that Shige's feelings won't be hurt.

Work through each extract in this way, finally writing a paragraph of interpretation on each one. You have now finished the whole question.

Christmas in Russia

Russia

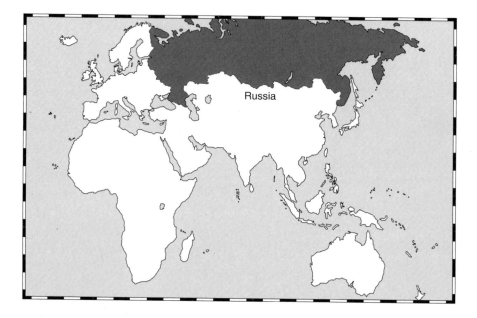

Introduction for the Teacher

Eugenie Fraser, born of a Russian mother and a Scottish father, was brought up in Russia in the days before the Revolution of 1917. The traditional Christmas described here was that of 1912. At that time Tsar Nicholas II still ruled the Russian Empire, but there had been unrest which Eugenie's parents, along with everyone else, knew all about. Tsar Alexander II had been assassinated and the perpetrators publicly hanged, and under Alexander III who succeeded him, there had been harsh repression of all forms of political dissent. Those who spread revolutionary ideas were expelled from universities and sent to Siberia and anyone caught plotting against the regime risked not only exile but death – Alexander Ulyanoff, the brother of Lenin, had been executed in 1887 for his part in plotting an attempt on the Tsar's life. Just the year before the Christmas in the extract, the Prime Minister Stolypin had been assassinated at the opera.

But for this Christmas at least, Eugenie and her prosperous family were secure and happy in Archangel, a town very far from Moscow on the northern shore of the White Sea. Although aware of these signs of unrest, the family could not know that there was far worse to come. There would only be one more Christmas before Russia was involved in the First World War, culminating in the 1917 Revolution and the murder of Nicholas II and the rest of his imperial family. However, all such tensions seemed far away when young Eugenie was dazzled by the celebrations and by the sight of her first Christmas tree.

The House by the Dvina

With the approach of Christmas a great activity commenced in the house. The floor polishers came and skated over the parquet floors in their inimitable style. Mirrors and furniture were rubbed until they shone, the chandelier was dismantled and each sparkling piece cleaned and hung back in its place. The same kind of activity went on in the kitchen. On the table, piled high, lay capercailzies[1], geese and white partridges, waiting to be plucked and prepared for the oven. A special dough, sitting in a crock for a month slowly fermenting and absorbing spices, was now ready to be rolled out and cut into stars, crescents and hearts and finally baked in the oven. Baskets were filled with these biscuits and, along with sweets and other delicacies, despatched to my Aunt Olga in Finland. Every day Babushka[2] set off into town and came back laden with parcels. Presents were sent to each of her numerous granddaughters and all the other members of the family including the nannies and mamkas[3]. No one was forgotten.

Christmas, as well as Babushka's and my own name-day of St Evgeniya, was to be celebrated as usual on Christmas Eve. As the day grew nearer, other more interesting, and for me, exciting and even mysterious preparations began upstairs. One evening immediately after dinner, Babushka produced a big bag of walnuts and placed it on the round table. Saucers of sweetened milk, lighted candles, sealing-wax and strands of green wool were laid out. Then each one of us was handed a small book of gold leaf attached to tissue pages. Marga and the boys knew the procedure. Marina, once she discovered what was wanted, worked faster than any of us. I tried to follow the best way I could. A single leaf,

---

[1] capercailzies: small game birds
[2] babushka: grandmother
[3] mamkas: wet nurses – women hired to breastfeed babies and very young children

attached to the tissue paper, was held in the palm of the hand. The walnut was dipped in the sweetened milk and immediately enveloped in gold. The two ends of the cut wool were placed on the flat end of the nut and sealed with a drop of sizzling wax. The nut, now ready for hanging, was placed on a tray.

Apples grown specially for the Christmas trade came next. These little apples, crimson and white, almost pear-shaped, were the type often depicted in fairy tales. The stalks on them were long enough to have attached to them the same green loops for hanging.

I had no idea for what purpose all these loops had to be fixed, nor yet did it occur to me to enquire. This coming Christmas was to be the first one I would remember. There was a vague memory of another one in Scotland, when in the morning I found a stocking full of little presents followed by other gifts and later by a Christmas party. In my early days in Scotland there were no Christmas trees.

In the mornings, rosy-cheeked peasant women, carrying baskets, came to the house offering their home-baked 'kazoolies' laid out in rows between layers of white linen. The 'kazoolies' were delicious spiced cakes formed into shapes of people and animals typifying the north. There were Eskimos, polar bears, reindeer, all decorated in white and pink sugar.

The doors leading into the ballroom were locked for some reason. Yura, Seryozha and Marga kept darting in and out, but gave vague answers or ignored completely all my enquiries. It was all very mysterious.

The house by now was rather full, but everyone was happy for in those days people still covered long distances, braving frosts and snowstorms to join family gatherings and above all to enjoy the gladness and warmth of an old-fashioned Russian Christmas.

As was the custom, Babushka and I received the usual congratulations on the day of our Saint. The presents that everyone brought vanished behind the locked doors of the ballroom. It was not usual for children to be running around between the feet of their elders, but later, it being Christmas, an exception was made. Meanwhile, the grown-ups adjourned to the corner room while all the children, under Marina's and Yura's supervision, were banished to the nursery. There we played games and amused ourselves, but I, full of curiosity, kept opening the door and peeping through to the dining-room where Babushka, with a preoccupied air, kept rearranging the hanging grapes on the epergnes[1] and putting finishing touches to the table. I saw Irisha, the young tablemaid, carrying through to the dining-room a tray loaded with hot pirozshkis[2] which would be served with the soup. I passed on the glad news to the others and sure enough we were soon trooping into the dining-room to take our places with our elders.

The Christmas dinner bore a resemblance to the one that I remembered in Scotland except that instead of roast turkey there were geese stuffed with apples accompanied by partridges cooked in sour cream. At the end as a special gesture to her half-Scottish granddaughter, Babushka served a plum pudding. Inside were the usual trinkets, which surprised and delighted young and old. During the dinner, there were pauses when someone would stand up and offer a toast to Babushka and myself in recognition of our name-day, which give me a delightful sense of importance.

Towards the end of dinner Yura and Seryozha excused themselves and disappeared into the ballroom. Soon after, Babushka suggested we should leave the table and move towards the closed doors. There we stood waiting. There was an air of expectation. Then, at the tinkling of a bell, all the lights went out, plunging the rooms in darkness. The double-doors were flung wide open.

And there, against the background of total darkness stood this glorious thing, stretching up to the ceiling, ablaze with lights. I had not seen before a Christmas tree of any kind. The sudden impact of this amazing sight overwhelmed me.

Everything shimmered and trembled. The beautiful fairy standing on tiptoes, the snow queen on the sledge driving the silver reindeer to her ice castle with the little boy behind her, Red Riding Hood with her basket setting off to visit her grandma, the

---

[1] epergnes: table ornaments, usually holding fruit or flowers
[2] pirozshkis: pies

little mermaid swaying gently on the edge of a branch, the princess in her gown and diamond coronet, the evil witch standing beside the cottage which is slowly circling on hen's feet, the gnomes and the little winged angels, the tinkling crystal icicles and the sparkling scattered frost. And over all the glitter, the characters out of fairy tales, the apples, sweets and golden walnuts, there was the brilliance of candles, each pointed flame surrounded by a golden halo encircling the tree, layer upon layer of them, and fusing together into one cascading light of dazzling splendour.

I still remember saying to myself, 'This must be like the heaven about which Babushka told me – the place where little children sometimes went to, where they were always happy and never scolded, where everything was bright and golden apples grew on trees.'

Happiness is relative – in my days I have had my share, but nothing has ever surpassed those few rare moments of sheer rapture when I stood gazing up at the wondrous sight of my first Christmas tree.

I could have stood for ever. Finally, I turned and walked over to my table. The presents for each member of the family were laid out on small individual tables. On mine there were many gifts. Babushka was distributing presents to all our friends and to every servant. The children were running round eating mandarin oranges and pulling nuts, apples and sweets from the tree.

Later there were slides displayed by a magic lantern on to a sheet hung over the wall of the hall. The scenes portrayed, from fairy tales and nursery rhymes, were accompanied by a running commentary by Seryozha and although we were to see these same pictures year after year they never failed to delight.

In the late evening the sledges of the guests began to glide back to their homes. After the last one left, Yura and Seryozha carried high steps into the ballroom and began to put out the candles. One by one the lights went out until the tree was left in darkness.

Eugenie Fraser

Assignments

1 What preparations are made in the household for the Christmas celebrations? What atmosphere is conveyed in the descriptions?

We'll start with the first part of the question:

> What preparations are made in the household for the Christmas celebrations?

To organize your answer, we'll divide the preparations up under four headings:
- the cleaning
- the food in the kitchen
- making the Christmas tree decorations
- the peasant women's offerings.

Starting with the cleaning, read the appropriate part of the passage for each heading. As you read, jot down notes on the different sorts of cleaning being carried out.
Use these notes to help you write several sentences about the cleaning.
This has been done for you as an example:

> *There was 'great activity' in the house as servants cleaned and polished ready for the Christmas party. Some standing on polishing cloths skated and slid over the parquet floors to make them shine as brightly as the polished furniture and mirrors. They took the chandeliers apart, cleaning each piece and reassembling them so that they sparkled.*

Now you are ready for the second part of the question:

> What atmosphere is conveyed in the descriptions?

You need to add at least two sentences explaining the atmosphere of these descriptions. Quoting particular words from the passage and commenting on how they contribute to the atmosphere is a good idea.

The first one has been finished for you:

> *The atmosphere is full of busy, energetic activity like polishing, rubbing and dismantling. This movement can be seen in the way the polishers 'skated' over the floors which is strong and energetic. The 'sparkling' pieces of the chandelier are part of the shiny, clean atmosphere of the house.*

Work through each of the other three headings in this way and you will then have completed the whole question.

---

2 Young Eugenie is delighted by the sight of her first Christmas tree. How does the writer convey the wonder of her experience?

The part of the passage which we are focusing on is when Eugenie sees the Christmas tree for the first time, from 'The double-doors were flung wide open' to 'when I stood gazing up at the wondrous sight of my first Christmas tree'.

The question asks **how** the writer conveys the young girl's wonder. This means that you are not just **describing** what Eugenie saw, but **analysing** the words the writer uses and explaining how they convey that wonder.

To make things easier, we'll make headings for you to work under:

⊕ words suggesting brilliance
⊕ words expressing drama and expectation
⊕ the effect of the sentence structure
⊕ the significance of the adult perspective.

To help you further, here are some points and questions for you to consider on each heading:

⊕ words suggesting brilliance

There are a great many words in these paragraphs suggesting sparkle, shine and brilliance, all of which helped to make Eugenie's experience so wonderful. Collect a long list and then colour code them according to nouns, verbs and adjectives. Explain separately their effect, giving plenty of examples.

⊕ words expressing drama and expectation
Make a collection of words and phrases which convey these qualities. Look particularly for verbs and adjectives. Colour code them and explain how they convey the drama and expectation which contribute to Eugenie's unforgettable experience.

⊕ the effect of the sentence structure
For each of the sentences in the long paragraph, count the number of sentences and the number of words in each. What is the effect of the very short sentence at the beginning? How does the length of the sentences help to convey Eugenie's sense of wonder and amazement?

⊕ the significance of the adult perspective
In what ways does the short paragraph at the end where the adult Eugenie looks back on that sight of her first Christmas tree help to emphasize how superb it was?

Write up one paragraph on each of these headings and you have then completed the whole question.

Munoo's Glimpse of the Circus
India/Pakistan

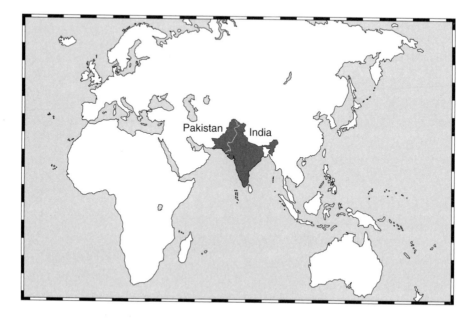

Introduction for the Teacher

Mulk Raj Anand was born in Peshawar, which is now in Pakistan, but was then part of the Indian Empire ruled by Britain. In 1948 the Indian Empire was divided up under Partition, a time of terrible violent protest, and Pakistan and India became separate countries.

Anand wrote in English and his main concern was, as he said, for 'the creatures in the lower depths of Indian society who were once men and women: the rejected who had no way to articulate their anguish against the oppressors.' Munoo in the story is one of the oppressed for whom Anand had such sympathy: a 'coolie', a servant of the lowest order.

Munoo is only a child and his dead mother a faint memory when he sets off from his hill village, forced to fend for himself. He finds a variety of cruelly harsh work from house servant and rickshaw driver to the 'dark, evil life' in a factory which makes pickles and chutney. Throughout all his hardship, he never loses his boy's spirit of adventure or his hope for a better life. In the following passage, he is looking for some kind of work in Daulatpur, when he hears the thumping of a drum and the city crier advertising the arrival of the circus. He is determined to see the show...

Coolie

He crept under cover of a small, filthy tent and waited tensely for a while. Then he looked towards the right and sighted an elephant coming soundlessly out of the entrance of the tent, followed by a crowd of city urchins, while a black driver sat on its head with his legs hidden under the ears of the beast.

'Do you know it dances, climbs on a ladder and plays a mouth organ,' one of the urchins was saying to his friend.

Munoo ran and joined the throng of boys.

One of the leaders of the throng mistook his caper for an invasion. He lifted his strip of a turban and threw it at the elephant's trunk. Jumbo swallowed it up after a graceful salute, as if it were a piece of straw.

Munoo returned the compliment by snatching the cap off the boy's head and throwing it to the elephant.

Before he knew where he was he had been caught by the neck by the youth. He swerved, and planting his leg against his opponent, flung him lightly into a ditch. As the young man struggled out, covered all over with slime, the urchins behind roared and screamed with laughter.

The elephant shied for a moment and the driver punched the beast with an iron handle, cursing Munoo the while. 'He started it first,' Munoo apologized. The driver jumped down and, catching Munoo by the ear, led him towards the trunk of the elephant to frighten him.

All the boys shied off screaming.

Munoo thought his last moment had come. But Jumbo only blew a heavy breath at his head and went on.

'I am not afraid,' Munoo said brazenly.

The driver smiled.

'All right,' the driver said. 'Go and call that grass-cutter who is going on the road, with the bundle of grass on his head.'

Munoo was only too willing to oblige, for he knew that if he came back with the grass-cutter he would get free access to the circus ground, where people were not admitted without a pass. He

ran for the grass-cutter. He caught him at the entrance of the
theatre stables and brought him back.

'I want to see the tamasha[1],' he said to the elephant driver,
currying favour with a humble smile, when the man had brought
the grass.

'Go away! Go away!' the driver said casually.

'Look,' Munoo insisted, 'I did that work for you.'

The man was walking away towards the back of the tent.
Munoo followed lightly behind. 'Look, I did that work for you!'
he repeated as they got well behind the tent.

'Don't pester me,' snapped the elephant driver. 'Sit down there,
anywhere, and see through the hole in the canopy.'

And he walked away.

Munoo looked for a hole in the canopy. There did not seem to
be one at first glance. He tried to lift it from a side.

'Don't do that,' the elephant driver's voice came sharp into his
ear. 'You will bring the whole tent down. Here!'

Munoo jumped towards a rent in the canvas in which the
elephant driver had dug the forefinger of his left hand.

The performance was well under way. The arena was packed in
a crescent of layer upon layer of chairs.

On the near side a band played European music, while under
the top of the tent a troupe of trapeze dancers had just brought off
a miraculous swing, flying from one end of space to another, till
their supple bodies came to a standstill and they walked out of the
arena.

Munoo's heart beat wildly at the cheering which followed. Then
its violent activity died down in the applause with which the
audience greeted Miss Tara Bai, who came swaying, almost like the
elephant, Munoo thought, that had swallowed his turban.

He could not see the details of her face through the rent in the
tent, but she acted like lightning as she lay down to accept a huge
stone on her stomach and rested calmly as two men beat the
stone with sledge hammers, in the way in which Munoo had seen
the coolies break huge boulders to make small stones for new

---

[1] tamasha: Urdu word for a public entertainment

roads. There was applause as she flung the weight off her body and stood bowing to the audience.

Munoo was spellbound.

But a noise of shuffling feet at a side entrance to the tent about twenty yards away on Munoo's left made him withdraw his eyes. It was only a white horse galloping into the arena.

He applied his eyes and saw the horse enter the ring, followed by a young man who wore what seemed to Munoo curiously tight angrezi[1] trousers and a long cloak of silver sequins. The man might have been a rubber doll the way he leapt from the ground on to the back of the fast-moving horse, stood balanced on its back for a moment, somersaulted, then balanced himself on his head with his legs stretched in the air, and slipped off lightly over the tail of his mount, as easily as if he were walking down marble stairs.

Munoo watched enraptured, his eyes wide open, his brain in a whirl at what seemed to be a miracle.

'I should like to do that,' he said to himself, wildly excited. But then the sight of the accomplished artist jumping from a very precarious position clean on to the back of his mount and galloping away seemed an impossible feat for him to imitate. 'He will be going to Vilayat[2] beyond the seas to where the Sahib-logs[3] come from,' Munoo thought. 'I cannot go there, anyway. I am only a coolie. But I will go to Bombay. Probably I might earn enough there to go beyond the black waters.'

From the midst of resounding cheers a couple of clowns seemed to have been born, dressed in comic hats and loose, spotted clothes, their faces painted white, red and black. They first played with a coloured ball, balancing it on the tips of their extended noses, then aped the trapeze dancers with hesitant movements, which somehow became perfect towards the end and created in Munoo just the effect they were intended to create.

The lion cages were coming in…

But Munoo was disturbed by the elephant driver who was passing.

---

[1] angrezi: foreign-style
[2] Vilayat: Britain
[3] Sahib-logs: British people

'Come, oh boy, do some work; help me to carry these buckets of water; you have seen enough of the circus now.'

It was hard for Munoo to tear himself away, but he felt that he owed the whole treat to the elephant driver and could not refuse to help. He rose limply from where he had crouched and followed the man.

Mulk Raj Anand

Assignments

1 From this lively passage, what do you learn about Munoo's character and his impressions of the circus performance?

This question is asking you to look at two aspects of Munoo:
- his character
- his impressions of the circus performance.

In preparation for writing about Munoo's character, make a list of four qualities of his character. Find a quotation from the story to support each one. The first one has been completed for you:

> *1 brave: "'I am not afraid," Munoo said brazenly.'*
> *2* _____
> *3* _____
> *4* _____

Having completed this, you can now explain more fully what each quotation shows about Munoo's character. Use the quality and quotation to expand into several complete sentences on each one. The first one has been done for you:

> *When the elephant driver jumped down and caught hold of Munoo's ear and led him towards the elephant's trunk, Munoo showed that he was brave. Although he was terrified and thought his 'last moment had come', he didn't show that he was afraid. As the elephant breathed on him, Munoo said brazenly 'I am not afraid'. 'Brazenly' shows that he was acting tougher and braver than he actually felt.*

When you have worked through your list in this way, you are ready for the second part of the question:
⊕ Munoo's impressions of the circus performance.

To organize your answer, we'll make headings:
⊕ the trapeze dancers
⊕ Miss Tara Bai
⊕ the man on the white horse.

Read the passage and as you read, jot down under each heading what Munoo finds impressive about each one. Then use your notes to write several sentences on each one.
The first one has been completed for you:

> When the trapeze artists were performing, Munoo was amazed by their 'miraculous swing' through space. He'd never seen anything like it before and to him it seemed 'miraculous', like magic. He admired their supple bodies and the cheering which followed made his heart beat 'wildly' with excitement.

When you have written about each of the headings in this way, you have answered the whole question.

2 How does the writer use language to convey the moods in this passage?

This task is much easier than it looks! It has two parts to it:
⊕ identifying the different moods in the passage
⊕ analysing the words used to convey the moods.

We'll think about the moods. A mood can be how someone in the passage is feeling, and also the atmosphere of the story. So read the passage and as you read, make a list of the changing moods and atmospheres. Add a quotation to support each mood. Your list could start like this:

1 *excitement:* 'Munoo watched enraptured, his eyes wide open, his brain in a whirl at what seemed to be a miracle.'
2 *liveliness:* 'As the young man struggled out, covered all over with slime, the urchins roared and screamed with laughter.'
3 _____
4 _____
5 _____

Complete the list of moods with their supporting quotations and then you are ready for the second part of the question:
⊕ analysing the words used to convey the moods.

Now you need to look at the words the writer uses and explain how they convey the particular mood. Look at features like:
⊕ the significance and meaning of words
⊕ verbs of movement
⊕ the effect of short and long sentences
⊕ the use of dialogue.

Using your ideas on these features, write several sentences on each of your moods, using your quotation and analysing the words. The first one has been done for you:

There is a mood of Munoo's wild excitement and sense of wonder, both when he is waiting for the circus and throughout the performance. 'Munoo watched enraptured, his eyes wide open, his brain in a whirl at what seemed to be a miracle.' His excitement is clear in this sentence. The writer's choice of vocabulary in 'enraptured' shows how magical the experience is for Munoo. His wide-open eyes suggest wonder and his brain is 'in a whirl', a violent commotion of impressions and excited feelings.

Now, work through all the moods on your list in this way, and you have completed the whole question.

Uncle Hong-do

South Korea

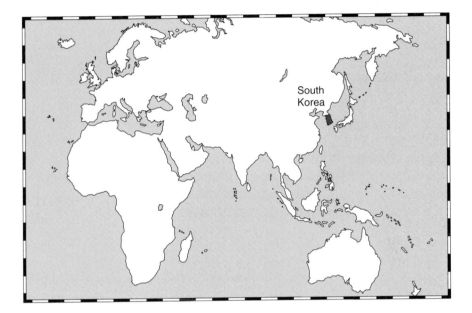

Introduction for the Teacher

This extract comes from Mira Stout's memoir of her Korean mother. Her mother's childhood was spent on her parents' idyllic estates in Korea which contained the one thousand chestnut trees of the book's title. By 1936, these estates were being confiscated by the Japanese, and the following year the Sino-Japanese war began, which greatly increased tension in Korea. There was Korean guerrilla resistance to the Japanese throughout her mother's childhood, and her teenage years were spent in war-torn Seoul, the capital, after the Korean War started in 1950. She finally had an opportunity to leave Korea and her family, and escaped to America in 1951. She married an American there and was to return to Korea only once in the next thirty years.

Hong-do, her mother's much younger brother, had been born after her escape to America. The only photograph of him she had was of a doll-like little boy in a sailor suit holding his mother's hand. In the early 1980's, when Mira was fourteen and her Uncle Hong-do only about five years older than herself, this virtual stranger was to come to their home in Vermont, USA.

The passage describes the reactions of the all-American Mira to this entirely foreign, 'spaceling' uncle. The unfamiliar guttural Korean language which he spoke with her mother at first separated them 'like barbed wire', but her attitude to Uncle Hong-do's apparent eccentricities gradually changed.

One Thousand Chestnut Trees

I saw Hong-do again at Easter. At home, snow still scabbed the fields, but the ground had thawed, and squelched underfoot. Wild gusts of fresh, sweet wind roared through the bare tree-tops. Unpacking my duffel bag, I resolved to be a bit kinder to my uncle – providing it was not too painful.

But I had forgotten little things about him – like the way he chewed spearmint gum with smacking gusto, and sang corny songs in the car. And his sense of humour! I rarely saw him laughing, but when he did, it was a razor-edged alto giggle. Then, at moments of unanimous family mirth he would be isolated in a deaf silence. He thought most American food was disgusting, and I never saw him reading a newspaper or book in English.

My uncle was like unconvertible currency; he refused to be tendered or melted down. There was no Western equivalent of his value. Sometimes I suspected he was simply saving himself so that he would not have to change again when he returned home.

Yet in my absence there were surprising developments. One afternoon as I studied for exams, I looked out at the faithful view of sloping, scrubby fields, towering pines, and immense sky, and noticed something peculiar about the row of younger trees opposite. Their lower branches had been brutally pruned to resemble topiary, but their trunks looked disastrously bald, like shorn poodle shanks. When I protested to my mother she smiled, and insisted that they now looked more like Korean bonsai; an observation gratingly inaccurate, to my affronted sensibilities.

Hong-do soon appeared back from Starksboro with a red and white striped parcel from Sam's Army-Navy Store, and went off to his room. As I was reading, something caught my eye out of the window; there was my uncle, zipped into a new track suit, vigorously touching his toes in the fresh air. I smiled patronizingly at his strict precision, exercising in the waist-high weeds as if in an indoor gym.

Then he stopped, approached a pine-bonsai, and playfully shook its slender truck. After an interval of staring, bull-like, at the tree, he suddenly charged at it, yelling murderously and began raining deft side-kicks and karate chops upon the little tree.

I rose from my chair. Had he gone mad? I heard my father's chair scraping in his studio, and ran off to confer with him. He had left his easel, and stood at the window watching Hong-do. Without speaking, we observed him warily circling the tree like a shadow-boxer, delivering the odd kick-chop. Dad finally rapped on the window-pane, and my uncle twisted round, confused and red-faced with exertion and waved at us enthusiastically. We laughed and waved back, marvelling. From then on, my uncle performed his *t'aekwondo*[1] exercises on the lawn without further interruptions.

After this, the atmosphere was lighter between us. *T'aekwondo* tree-attacks seemed to relax Hong-do, he smiled more readily, and began to look quite as handsome as his photographs. This unexpected glimpse of him lent a wider circumference to my mean perception of his character.

Still, an unnavigable distance separated us. I regarded him more as an exotic zoo tiger than as my only living uncle. It was safe to observe him through bars, to admire him wryly from the window, but I couldn't begin to relinquish those barriers. The schoolyard bullies who had kicked me behind the apple trees with their pointy-toed cowboy boots might come running back through the years to punish me again for having oriental blood.

Hong-do's foreignness might be contagious; I could be ostracized not only for harbouring an alien, but for becoming more of one myself. With my layers of sportswear and Celtic freckles I could pass for Caucasian, but my uncle's incriminating features might give me away. It would be wiser to stay clear of him until my immunity was established. My secret Korean half was exiled to a remote inner gulag that even I was unable to find.

In the evenings, reading after supper, I sometimes caught Hong-do staring unhappily out of the window into the dark woods

---

[1] t'aekwondo: Korean martial art

beyond his own cantilevered reflection. Only then did I regret not being a confidante. With the dumb instinct of a golden retriever, I itched to go out into the darkness and bring him back inside again, but just on the point of speaking to him, decided I was too small and unqualified for such a rescue. It was beyond me.

It was easier to pretend that he was not quite human. I don't remember asking him much about our relations in Seoul, or why he had come to the West when life seemed to be so pleasing there. What was he thinking of when he was so quiet at the dinner table? What did he miss about Korea? Would he have liked to learn to ski? I allowed his elementary English to deter me from asking.

By my uncle, for his part, was maddeningly opaque. His eyes were so black that I couldn't see his pupils. It was *me* that I saw squinting back irritably from those distant planets. His silences alone were new desert continents, exposing me as a mere water-dependent speck.

Yet Hong-do could be alarmingly vocal. Sometimes he would pluck away at Beatles chords on my old, badly-tuned guitar, yodelling 'Yesterday' plaintively from his room. To my distress, he and my mother also sang rapturous Korean songs together in the study, in a twangy, throbbing oriental vibrato which sounded surreal, and faintly sinister in the puritan Vermont woods. I was glad we had no neighbours.

Why did they *wail* like that?

'Because we express *han*,' said Hong-do good-naturedly.

And what on earth was *han*?

There was a long pause.

'*Han* is sorrow and yearning and resentment; it lasts centuries, and never goes away. It is at the core of us,' said my mother.

But what were the words?

Another pause.

'*Han* is so deep, that it comes before language.'

I rolled my eyes at my father, hoping to enlist his support, but he looked away. Then I went to my room, and drowned out the *han* with the more familiar ululations of Neil Young.

I remember one final episode that Easter holiday. As I was studying one afternoon at my usual place by the window,

Hong-do slipped into the kitchen to toast some seaweed. After offering me a warm, sulphurous black square – which I ate, grudgingly – he went outdoors to join my mother in the garden.

Then, I heard a yell, and saw Hong-do push my mother aside, his eyes locked to the ground. Running out to see what was wrong, I found Hong-do down on all fours, stabbing spasmodically at the earth with a trowel. Now quite inured to his unpredictable ways, I asked casually what he was doing.

' A grass snake,' said my mother.

'But they're harmless,' I said, popping my eyes.

'Maybe, but to him, serpents are a symbol of evil, and should be destroyed.'

My uncle had lost sight of the snake, and was shouting at my mother in Korean.

'What's he saying now?' I piped.

'He can't believe that we allow snakes to pollute our land,' she said neutrally, as if unsure of where she herself stood on the matter. Still muttering, Hong-do was crouched in a combat stance in the dead asparagus patch, gingerly parting weeds with his trowel. I wished him luck insincerely, and went back indoors. Minutes later, my parents left on an errand.

Hong-do came indoors, and began rummaging angrily through drawers and cupboards. Next, he changed into his new Wrangler jeans, my father's too-big rubber boots and wood-chopping gloves. He'd even produced a fireman-style slicker from somewhere, cuffs rolled neatly. Then, he left without a word, carrying a long, fat stick he'd found beneath the porch.

'Unbelievable,' I muttered, looking around reflexively to see if anyone could confirm what I was seeing. Being alone, I shook my head and returned to the reassuring mental hygiene of my algebra book. But now and then I looked up at the field expectantly.

My mother and father returned from town with the groceries, and asked after Hong-do, smiling when they heard about his hunting preparations. We watched a muted sunset, and took tea and Chinese steam buns in the sitting room, half-listening to the news on the radio. I felt too ruffled by my uncle's eccentric behaviour to concentrate.

Just then the front door opened, and Hong-do stamped in, displaying a small green snake by its tail as if it were a ten-foot swordfish. Dutifully, my parents admired his catch while I trained a sceptical eye on the pitiful reptile. Then, however, I caught a glimpse of my uncle's expression, which shamed me. The pride brimming in his eyes was remarkable and disconcerting. His pride was so intense that I almost found myself wishing I could see the snake as he saw it. I stared at it hard, hoping for something magic to happen; but nothing did. My doubt remained and divided us.

Mira Stout

Assignments

1 Explain Mira's mixed feelings towards her Uncle Hong-do.

To answer a broad question like this, you need to have a clear focus in your answer. We'll limit ourselves to analysing Mira's mixed feelings in three distinct incidents:
- Uncle Hong-do's t'aekwondo exercises
- Uncle Hong-do and Mira's mother expressing 'han'
- Uncle Hong-do and the grass snake.

These incidents will give you plenty of material from which to comment on Mira's different feelings towards her uncle. Start with reading the part of the passage about Uncle Hong-do's t'aekwondo exercises. As you read, write down the feelings Mira experienced as she watched him. You will have notes like:

shocked to see the trees cut
thought Uncle looked a bit silly in his tracksuit
angry when he started kicking the tree
felt different when he waved
admired his skill
glad that the t'aekwondo calmed him down a bit

Uncle Hong-do

Now, using the notes you have made whilst reading, write one or two sentences on each of the feelings you have identified.
Quoting words and phrases from the passage to support your points is a good idea.
The first one has been completed for you:

Mira had been shocked to see the trees in her 'faithful' view pruned to look like 'shorn poodle shanks'. She felt her own trees had been ruined because of some whim of her foreign uncle to make them like Korean bonsai. When she first saw Uncle Hong-do in his new tracksuit exercising, she smiled at him 'patronizingly' which suggests that she felt she was a superior Westerner and her uncle an eccentric foreigner. But when she saw him kicking and chopping the tree and heard him 'yelling murderously', she felt he had gone too far and was angry. When her father rapped on the window and Uncle Hung-do just waved cheerily back, her feelings changed. She and her father waved back 'marvelling'. Her anger had changed to admiration, 'marvelling', and from then on she was happy to see the calming effect the t'aekwondo had on her uncle.

Follow the same routine for the other two incidents, and then you have completed the whole question.

2 Analyse the writer's use of language in the following extracts.

   a *My uncle was like unconvertible currency; he refused to be tendered or melted down. There was no Western equivalent of his value. Sometimes I suspected he was simply saving himself so that he would not have to change again when he returned home.*

   b *Still an unnavigable distance separated us. I regarded him more as an exotic zoo tiger than as my living uncle. It was safe to observe him through bars, to admire him wryly from the window, but I couldn't begin to relinquish those barriers.*

   c *Hong-do's foreignness might be contagious; I could be ostracized not only for harbouring an alien, but for becoming more of one myself. It would be wiser to stay clear of him until my immunity was established. My secret Korean half was exiled to a remote inner gulag that even I was unable to find.*

d *Being alone, I shook my head and returned to the reassuring mental hygiene of my algebra book. But now and then I looked up at the field expectantly.*

In this question, you are going to **analyse** the writer's use of language in some lines from the passage. This means you'll be:
- looking closely at the writer's language and sentence structure
- explaining how they convey to you the meaning and atmosphere of the passage.

Read each extract carefully and afterwards look at these sorts of features:
- metaphor and simile: do they perhaps heighten the idea of foreignness and, if so, how?
- adjectives: how do they add to the meaning and atmosphere?
- a long sentence: does it tell you something about Mira's state of mind?

Explain how the features you find in the extracts help to convey meaning and effects.

The first one has been done for you as an example:

a *The writer is conveying the way that Uncle Hong-do stood out as totally different and foreign by comparison to the people familiar to Mira. She expresses this idea effectively by using the metaphor of money sustained throughout, in 'currency' which can't be 'tendered', 'value' and 'saving'. This gives the impression that everything about Uncle Hong-do was totally foreign to Mira, and she felt that he was determined to retain his national identity. Because of the associations of currency, there is also the suggestion that Mira recognized Uncle Hong-do's worth and value.*

Following this example, work through the three other extracts. You have now completed the whole question.

Vodka

Russia

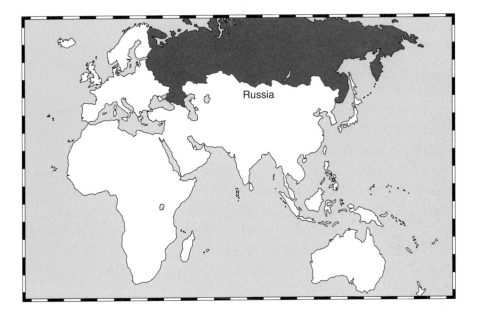

Russia

Introduction for the Teacher

Vodka first appeared in Poland, and then Russia, as a medicine. When beer or wine was left outside in winter, the water content would freeze, leaving, it was realized, a higher-strength residue beneath. This was used externally to treat cuts or was made into an ointment for painful joints. After mass production started in the fifteenth century, vodka was swallowed as a medicine for colds and bad stomachs. Only in the eighteenth century did vodka begin to be drunk for pleasure; the method of drinking was integral to that pleasure and remains unchanged today. Vodka is swallowed in one gulp from the glass but never, unless by the most desperate alcoholic, from the bottle. Nor would a Russian ever add anything to vodka, the purest alcoholic drink on earth.

Vitali Vitaliev writes here about what vodka means to him as a Russian. He grew up in the Soviet Union of the Communist period when there were laws against distilling one's own vodka, but these were abused. Vitaliev left Moscow for London in 1990, before the break-up of the Soviet Union and the downfall of Communism. He writes with wit whilst conveying the tragic enormity of the problem which alcoholism poses in today's Russia.

The Last Eighteen Drops

The only times a bottle of vodka would appear on our family table were during the infrequent visits of my father's uncle Pavel, who lived in Dnepropetrovsk and was a colonel in the Soviet Army. I liked his visits. After a couple of shots he would become facetious and tell funny stories about his army life, and I enjoyed the sight of his rough military tunic hanging on the clothes rack in the corridor next to my father's raincoat. It smelled of war and adventure. When Uncle Pavel was in a particularly good mood (usually after three or four shots of vodka), he would even allow me to play with his cockaded[1] service-cap.

It wasn't until I was about seven that I realized how dangerous, even lethal, vodka could be. My parents told me that a young man who lived in the neighbouring block of flats, and whom I had often seen playing dominoes on the battered wooden table in our courtyard, had died. When I asked my grandmother why, she made a serious face and mumbled: '*Zgorel ot vodki*' (literally: 'He burned himself to death with vodka'). It was hard for me to imagine how a plain, water-like liquid could kill (let alone burn to death) someone so big and strong. I remember peeping – with the other kids – into the basement flat where the domino player lay in state, covered with wreaths and fir-tree branches. His father – an old man, who had drunk vodka with his son but had survived – shooed us away.

YEVGENY BULAVIN

When I was sixteen, in the summer holidays before my final year at school, I went with a classmate to a sports camp near the village of Gaidary. The camp was in desperate need of kitchen staff, and we volunteered to work as dishwashers in the canteen.

It was here that I met Yevgeny Bulavin. He was a second-year student of physical culture, and at eighteen, he was almost a patriarch in our eyes. He was also an alcoholic, but we didn't realize it then. We were eager to imitate him. We would finish

---

[1] cockaded: with a rosette or badge of office

washing-up after dinner at around eleven p.m. Then, under Yevgeny's expert guidance, we would scour the camp in search of something to drink. This is how, for the first and last time in my life, I came to drink perfume. It was called 'Russian Forest' and when we diluted it with water, the opaque liquid in each glass rose with a soapy foam. For the rest of the evening, we stank like three walking barber's shops.

Few things in life were capable of making Yevgeny as distraught as he was as the sight of an empty vodka bottle. Having placed the 'dead' bottle horizontally on the table, like a perished soldier laid to rest by his comrade-in-arms, he would watch it closely, trying to hypnotize it into filling up with vodka again. His theory was that no matter how empty the bottle might seem, there would always be eighteen drops of vodka left in it. After several minutes of silent grieving he would lift the bottle from the table, turn it upside down, and shake it over a glass. Miraculously, eighteen indolent vodka drops would indeed slide from its neck, one after another. Not sixteen, not nineteen, but invariably eighteen. You can check it yourself. Some abstruse physical law is hiding inside those empty bottles.

He was a sportsman, a home-grown philosopher, a draft dodger (he simulated dromomania, an irrepressible passion for purposeless travel) and, I suppose, my drinking supervisor. His favourite toast was 'To this glass not being the last one, to more frequent drinking – long live alcohol – hooray!' Passing a drunkard lying in the gutter he would say: 'Happy guy! Look, he is already enjoying himself, and we haven't drunk anything yet!'

Yevgeny's favourite haunt was the shabby hut of the village home-brewer known throughout the area as 'Baba Lena' (Granny Lena). She produced *samogon* – a stinking potato spirit – on an almost industrial basis. Home-brewing in the Soviet Union was a serious criminal offence, but Baba Lena was ingenious. She would post her old husband, shrunk from decades of heavy drinking, at the front gate. 'Speak up: I can't hear you!' he would mutter to visitors, as he studied them with the eyes of a cunning Ukrainian peasant. Then he would yell, without turning his head: 'Lena! Have we got anything left?' From inside a nearby shed, a woman's voice would echo in Ukrainian: 'Yeah. Just a tiny bit. Have they got an empty container?'

And then you would hear the hissing and rattling sounds of their sophisticated moonshine machinery starting up.

It was not long before we were blacklisted by the cautious Baba Lena. It happened after Yevgeny tried (unsuccessfully) to catch one of her chickens to diversify our camp diet. Eventually, Baba Lena herself was arrested and sent to prison as a 'threat to the law and order of the whole of the Severski Donets region', as a local newspaper put it.

THE SHOE-POLISH SANDWICH

Three years later, as a second-year university student, I took a summer job as a sleeping-car attendant. Each railway carriage had two attendants working alternate shifts. My fellow worker, Mitrich, was an old man with an amazing capacity for vodka. He drank two half-litre bottles three times a day, locking himself in his compartment and gulping each dose down within the space of five to ten minutes. Then he would attend to his chores: checking tickets, sweeping the carriage floors and taking small bribes (usually in the form of vodka) from stowaways. A litre of vodka didn't have much effect on him, though his normally expressionless eyes would start gleaming. 'Wine is bad for you, but vodka is very healthy,' he would say. 'Doctors recommend it.'

Officially, the railway was a no-drinking zone. But this did not inhibit the staff on our train. The chief attendant would routinely ransack the compartments of his subordinates in search of a drink and would confiscate (and consume) anything with an alcohol content: vodka, beer, perfume, shampoo, toothpaste or even shoe polish, which he used to spread on a slice of bread (shoe-polish sandwiches were supposed to give you a mildly inebriated feeling – I didn't try one myself).

One night, when I was on duty in carriage thirteen, smoking a cheap Cuban cigar so as not to fall asleep, I had a visit from the engine driver himself. He was eager to share a bottle of vodka with me. I could see that he was already so stoned he could hardly walk. All the while, the train kept roaring along. The driver explained that he had left the engine on 'autopilot' as there were no scheduled stops for the next 200 kilometres. He also assured me that his young assistant was still in the driver's cabin, just in case, although the latter was apparently so drunk that he couldn't stand either. It took a considerable effort – mental and physical – to persuade the driver to return to his post.

On our train's forty-eight-hour journey from the Black Sea coast to the Baltic, there was also only one station which had a vodka shop in the vicinity. The train stopped there for only ten minutes. An hour before the vodka stop, Mitrich would become agitated. As the train approached the station, he would stand on a footboard with an empty pillowcase in his hand. Then he would leap off while the train was still moving, and race to the vodka shop. Ten minutes was barely long enough, and he would usually jump back on to the train when it was already sliding along the platform. Several vodka bottles would be jingling amicably inside the pillowcase.

Since my father was a nuclear physicist, he was allowed pure alcohol for cleaning the optical instruments at his office. What he didn't use he would bring home. My father kept the alcohol in an unlocked cupboard, where it was soon discovered by Yevgeny Bulavin, who had become a frequent guest at the flat after our dishwashing stint. 'Your father's optical equipment won't suffer if the liquid is not exactly ninety-six per cent proof,' said my drinking tutor. So one day, when my father was at work, we poured out half of the spirit and topped the bottle up with tap water. We drank the alcohol straight off, on the balcony. It was like swallowing a ball of fire. The alcohol had to be washed down immediately with water to avoid burning your intestines. One of the nastiest tricks played on me by Yevgeny was to offer me another glass of the spirit as a chaser, instead of water. I nearly choked to death.

MINE'S A LARGE TOOTH-POWDER

Later, I drank more routinely, in Moscow drinking sessions with my friends: a bottle of vodka in the centre of the table, and the telephone covered with a cushion – the KGB's bugs were everywhere – to give us a naive illusion of privacy.

Drinking under Communism was not hedonistic. It provided us with an outlet – a coveted, even if short-term, escape from political dogma and social gloom. A bottle of vodka was therefore a sort of liquid hard currency, much more reliable (and much more stable) than money. Anything, from a trip abroad to difficult-to-obtain roof tiles, could be bought and sold for alcohol, and had its inflation-proof vodka equivalent.

But at the end of the 1980s Mikhail Gorbachev attempted to curb his country's near-endemic alcoholism. Countless sobriety societies, which every worker was forced to join (fees were simply deducted from salaries), sprang up like mushrooms after a good July rain. These societies were staffed for the most part by carefully vetted bureaucrats from the uneven ranks of heavy drinkers and chronic alcoholics. They did nothing apart from organizing politically correct 'sober' birthday parties and wedding ceremonies, during which vodka was covertly poured from samovars and kettles. Alcohol was hard to find in the shops. The effect was predictable: vodka-deprived drunks took to shampoo, glue, perfume, insect repellent and window cleaner. In a Moscow park, I once saw three drunks boiling tooth powder in an empty can on top of a bonfire. They boiled it for five hours (or so they said), then carefully removed the alcohol from the top with tablespoons, drank it – and immediately started vomiting.

Vodka came back in a flood after Gorbachev went. Westerners assumed that with the collapse of Communism, people in the former Soviet Union would drink less – a democratic society would provide alternative forms of escape: books, a free media, foreign travel, the cornucopia of consumer goods. The reality has been different. Drinking in the post-Communist world has increased dramatically since the fall of the Berlin Wall.

Vitali Vitaliev

Assignments

1 As Vitaliev grew up, how did the drinkers he encountered develop his understanding of the effects of vodka?

Vitaliev writes about various people he has known at different stages in his life who drink vodka. What he saw of these people over the years developed his understanding of vodka and its effects. The question is asking you to:
⊕ identify these people
⊕ explain their experiences
⊕ explain what Vitaliev learned about vodka from them.

So, first of all we'll list the vodka drinkers whom Vitaliev knew. There are five in the passage. The first two have been selected for you:

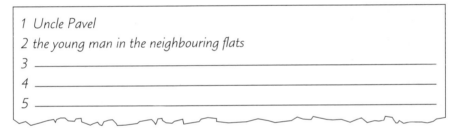

1 Uncle Pavel
2 the young man in the neighbouring flats
3 _____
4 _____
5 _____

Complete the list and then read carefully the sections in which these people appear and write down notes and brief quotations. Next, use these notes to explain in a paragraph under each heading:
⊕ the person's experience of vodka
⊕ what Vitaliev learned about vodka from him/her.

The paragraph on the first heading has been completed for you:

When young Vitaliev's Uncle Pavel visited his home, he drank vodka which made him talkative and good natured. He told funny stories about army life and let little Vitaliev play with his special army hat. His parents didn't drink alcohol, so this was a new experience for Vitaliev. He liked Uncle Pavel's stories about the army and the smell of 'war and adventure' on his army tunic.

When you have explained the experience, you need to cover the final bullet point:

⊕ what Vitaliev learned about vodka from him/her.

Now, add some sentences which explain what Vitaliev then understood about vodka and its effects.
The first paragraph has been completed for you:

At this stage, Vitaliev was only a child and he had limited understanding of the effects of vodka. He had no idea whether vodka was good or bad. He just knew it was what made his Uncle Pavel tell exciting stories which he loved to hear.

You can now write up your paragraphs on the other people in this way. You will then have completed your answer to the question.

2 Explain in detail how the last section, 'Mine's a large tooth-powder', contrasts with the rest of the passage.

This question is asking you to make a comparison between the last section of the passage and what comes before it. You will need to structure your answer, so we'll make topic headings of the features you'll be looking at:

⊕ the use of narrative and anecdote
⊕ the use of direct speech
⊕ the humour
⊕ the author's opinions.

Read the article carefully jotting down notes as you read. You are going to use the notes to write under these topic headings. You want to make sure that you compare both sections of the passage, so make two columns headed:

1 Mine's a large tooth-powder
2 The rest of the passage

The first topic heading has been completed for you:

	Mine's a large tooth-powder	The rest of the passage
The use of narrative and anecdote	It's not a story any more. There's only the one short anecdote of the drunks in the Moscow park. This makes it much more serious because there are no funny bits like before. It means there's no relief from the shocking facts he is giving us.	There are plenty of anecdotes about real people like Mitrich and Bulavin. These anecdotes are sometimes funny, like Bulavin's theory of the eighteen drops. The author's message that vodka is destructive is clear, but the stories make it entertaining at the same time. The anecdotes make the message easier to digest. People wouldn't read it without them because it would be too serious.
The use of direct speech		
The humour		
The author's opinion		

You are now ready to write up your paragraphs under each topic heading. You need to make the comparison between your two columns using words and phrases to link them such as:

⊕ in comparison with
⊕ in contrast to

Remember That You are Mine
Nigeria

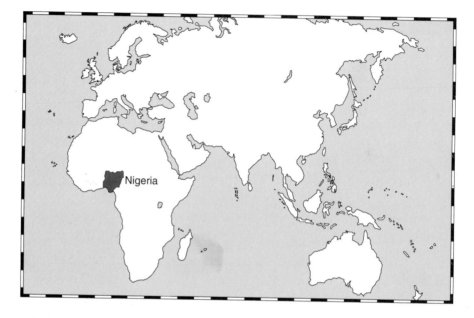

Introduction for the Teacher

Buchi Emecheta was born in 1944 near Lagos, Nigeria in West Africa where she went to a missionary school. She was orphaned young, and when she was sixteen she was married to the young man she had been engaged to since the age of eleven. When she was only eighteen, she came to live in England with her husband. After her six-year marriage ended, Buchi Emecheta was left with five children to care for.

Her novel *The Bride Price* explores the disadvantageous role of women in Nigerian society and this extract comes from the first chapter. Aku-nna, the daughter who knows that the only good she is to her father is as the bride price she will fetch for him when she is married, is based on Buchi Emecheta's first-hand experience.

Aku-nna's parents, Ma Blackie and Ezekiel Odia, married before the Second World War and had two children: Aku-nna, now thirteen, and her brother, Nna-nndo, now eleven. Ezekiel fought for the British during the Second World War in Burma and served in India and suffered an injury to his foot which has still not healed properly after five years. Ma Blackie is a fine, tall woman for whom Ezekiel paid a high bride price, but she has disappointed her husband: since his return from the war, she has not produced another son. Ma Blackie is desperate to produce more sons for her husband – Aku-nna being of little use, as she is a girl – and at this point in the story, she has gone back to her home town of Ibuza to plead with the river goddess to give her more babies. The children's father, whom they call Nna, should be at work in the railway yard, but when Aku-nna and Nna-nndo come home from school, they find him at home. Something is obviously bothering him.

The Bride Price

Aku-nna knew that she was too insignificant to be regarded as a blessing to this unfortunate marriage. Not only was she a girl but she was much too thin for the approval of her parents, who would rather have a strong and plump little girl for a daughter. Aku-nna just would not put on weight, and this made her look as if she was being starved; but she simply had not the kind of healthy appetite her brother Nna-nndo had. And that was not the end of the disgrace she was showering on her family. If a child at the other end of Akinwunmi Street had chicken-pox, Aku-nna was bound to catch it; if someone else at the bottom of the yard had malaria, Aku-nna would have her share too. For her it was forever a story of today foot, tomorrow head, the day after neck, so much so that her mother many a time begged her to decide once and for all whether she was going to live to die. One thing Ma Blackie could not stand, she said over and over again, was a 'living dead', an *ogbanje*.

Ezekiel Odia often pitied his daughter, particularly because she took more after him than his Amazon of a wife. She was small, Aku-nna was, not so much in height as in bone structure, and she was not at all dark, her skin that kind of pale brown colour one gets after putting too much milk in chocolate. Her eyes were large like her father's, but open and translucent; their brownness always had a special glow when she was happy and excited and when she was sad the glimmer disappeared. She had not developed the red criss-crosses which her father had in the whites of his eyes, but Ezekiel knew that, except for the fact that she promised to be a fairly tall woman, his daughter was his very image. He had named her Aku-nna, meaning literally 'father's wealth', knowing that the only consolation he could count on from her would be her bride price. To him this was something to look forward to.

Aku-nna on her part was determined not to let her father down. She was going to marry well, a rich man of whom her father would approve and who would be able to afford an expensive bride price. She would have her marriage first of all solemnized by the beautiful goddess of Ibuza, then the Christians would sing her a wedding march – 'Here comes the bride' – then her father Nna would call up the spirits of his great, great-grandparents to guide her, then after all that, and only after all that, would she leave her father's house.

But on this hot day, when the sun was pouring its merciless fire onto the unprotected heads of children coming home from school, when the heat was so intense that the ground looked as though it had been cooked and then baked, when the heat ate its way through the shoeless feet of Africans padding their various ways to their various destinations, when the air was so still, so waterless, so juiceless, that perspiration had to pour from the bodies of humans to neutralize the temperature – Aku-nna forgot all thoughts of her bride price, and felt a kind of closeness to which she could not give name binding her to her father. She moved nearer to him, and watched a big bead of perspiration working its way, snake-like, down the ridge of Nna's nose; reaching the wide part where his nose formed two black, funnel-like nostrils, this big stream of perspiration hesitated for a while, then, just like the great River Niger breaking into tributaries, divided into tinier strands. One or two of the tiny strands dropped onto Nna's mouth. He did not lick them, but wiped them away.

Then he spoke, his voice very thick: 'They want me to come to the hospital to see to my foot. I shall not be long. I shall be back for the evening meal.'

The children looked down at their father's ailing foot. That stupid foot, Aku-nna thought to herself, always gave her father a great deal of trouble. It was the effect of the war. That much she had been told by many of their relatives, especially old Uncle Richard who had been to the war as well. But he was more communicative than their father. Uncle Richard told the children that the white British could not bear the swamp in Burma and India and so they made West African soldiers stand in for them. Their father was lucky to come back alive, he told the children, because many African soldiers died, not from Hitler's bombs but from the conditions they were subjected to. They were either eaten up by the mosquitoes in the Burmese jungle or bitten up by water snakes in India. Aku-nna did not know which of these calamities had actually befallen her father, but one of his feet had a nasty scar that had healed badly and this foot had a way of getting swollen at any change in weather. It had been plastered over, it had been prayed upon, but it still swelled up at odd times. Now the leg had started to cause Nna pain again and this strain showed however much he tried to hide it. There was a slight swelling in the other foot, too, but both feet were shod in a pair of khaki work shoes and did not look at all bad compared to the way they usually were during the rainy season. So why did Nna seem so unhappy? If all he was going to do was to go to the hospital on Lagos Island for a check up, and if he would be back for the evening meal, then why was he looking so guilty, so disturbed?

Aku-nna did not ask her father this aloud, but the thought was there in her mind, muddled but persistent. She sighed with relief, though, that there was no cause for alarm. Nna would be back for the evening meal. If she had been a grown-up she would have scolded him, saying: 'But you scared us so! Standing there as if you have seen a ghost.' However in Nigeria you are not allowed to speak in that way to an adult, especially your father. That is against the dictates of culture. Despite that, some little maternal instinct in her told her that he could do with a bit of reassurance. She was now so close that she could touch him.

She laid her small hand on one of his and said: 'I'm going to make you Nsala soup[1], very hot, with lots of pepper, and the pounded yam I shall prepare to go with it will be lumpless. So, Nna, hurry back home to eat your evening meal hot. I know you don't like it cold.'

---

[1] Nsala soup: very hot, spicy soup made with chicken or fish

Nna smiled. His reddened eyes focused on his daughter, the corners of the eyes formed small wrinkles and his white teeth gleamed. For a while the woebegone expression on his sick and bloated face disappeared.

'Thank you, my little daughter, but don't boil more yams than you can pound. That *odo*[1] handle is too heavy for you. Don't do too much pounding.' He picked up his felt work hat, which he had put on a chair, and adjusted it on his shaved head, pulling the brim down a little in front of his eyes and then padding the sides into shape. 'The key to the big cupboard is in my grey trousers – you know, the ones hanging on the hook on the wall. If you want any money, you take it from the big cupboard, but be very careful how you spend it, because you have to make it go a very long way.'

If the children thought to themselves, 'But you'll be coming back in time for the evening meal tonight,' they were now too frightened to say. For not only would it be rude, but also Nna's face, after his brief smile, had assumed the finality of a closed door. He became brisk, just like someone preparing for a final departure. His hands, blackened by years of working in the railway foundry, touched this and that, picking things up and putting them down again. He told them to be good children to their mother and to respect all adults. He told them that they should try to be a glory to his name, because he cared for them, because they were his life.

Eventually Nna came to the door, saying that he had to go now. Then he added: 'Always remember that you are mine.'

His small lips were shaking and he pressed them together as if he was trying desperately to hold himself from crying. Involuntarily, as if hypnotized against their will, the children drew nearer, their young eyes following the movements of their father's eyes, which by now had grown so big that they seemed to be standing out in relief on his black forehead rather than inside his head. He acted as if in a hurry. He patted Nna-nndo on his inky head, touched Aku-nna slightly on the cheek and went out of the door.

Buchi Emecheta

---

[1] *odo*: heavy wooden paddle used for pounding yams

Assignments

1 What happened to alarm Aku-nna and Nna-nndo when they returned home after school and found their father at home?

This is a straightforward question, but you need to make sure that you focus on the **key words** in the question:

What happened **to alarm**...

Read the passage and as you read, take notes on the children's father, writing down brief quotations to support your points, under the following headings:
- what their father looked like
- how their father behaved
- what their father said.

When you have finished your notes, write a full paragraph on each heading. Remember to focus on what alarmed the children and to quote appropriately. The paragraph on the first heading has been written for you:

> *Aku-nna thought her father looked as though he had seen a ghost. He was sweating and pain showed in his face, which was fixed in a 'woebegone expression'. Aku-nna thought he looked unhappy, 'guilty' and 'disturbed' which alarmed her. Her father's leg and foot looked no worse than it had often been, so she was afraid that something worse might be wrong.*

Write your notes up into a paragraph for each of the other headings, and then you have completed the question.

2 What do you learn about the cultural background to the story?

This passage comes from the first chapter from a novel which is set in Nigeria, in Africa. Reading it tells you a good deal about the place and the culture of the people. To organize your answer, we'll focus on five different topics:

⊕ why Aku-nna feels a disappointment to her parents
⊕ the African and Christian religious beliefs and customs
⊕ the variations of climate referred to
⊕ the father's war experiences
⊕ the code of behaviour between the children and their father.

Read the passage and as you read, take notes under each of the headings. You will find more detail on some topics than others. With your notes, write down brief quotations which support some of the points you are making. Quote words and phrases only, not long sentences. Then, using these notes and quotations, write a detailed paragraph on each heading.
The first one has been done for you:

> *Aku-nna knows she is a disappointment to her parents because not only is she a girl, but she's thin and picks up illnesses which are 'disgraces' she feels she 'showers' on her family. She feels she has covered them in shame. Her mother cruelly calls her an 'ogbanje', a 'living dead', because she looks so unhealthy. Girls' only use in this culture is as brides for their fathers to sell and Aku-nna's name, meaning literally 'father's wealth' means she can't escape this fact. But she knows she won't be an easy bride to sell. To her parents, the family consists of 'an only son' and she's heard them arguing about her mother's failure to produce another son, the only worthwhile child to have. As a girl, Aku-nna is not valued.*

When you have written a paragraph on each of the other headings, you have completed the question.

Plague
Japan

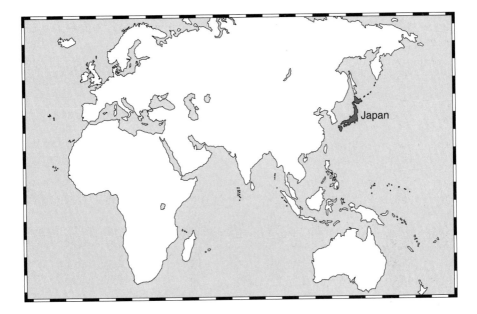

Introduction for the Teacher

Although not published in the UK until 1995, the novel from which this extract comes was published in Japan in 1958 when its author was twenty-three. It is a violent, burning protest against war and violence. The story is a grim one and makes an interesting parallel with William Golding's *Lord of the Flies* (1954). Golding's characters were English, Kenzaburo Oë's Japanese but these national boundaries do not matter. The strength of both texts is the universality of their message and the power with which it is expressed.

Oë was born in 1935 and brought up in a mountain valley deep in the mountainous interior of Shikoku, the most isolated and conservative of Japan's four main islands. His childhood was a time of war and upheaval for Japan, and the remoteness of his birthplace gave him an unusual vantage point, that of being Japanese but something of an outsider. At school, a ritual was observed. The teacher asked each pupil, 'What would you do if the Emperor asked you to die?' and each child would answer 'I would cut open my belly and die, sir.' Oë knew when he made this reply that his answer was a lie. His youthful anti-war fervour was further fuelled by the death of his father in the Second World War. Another defining moment for Oë was hearing the Emperor himself announcing on the radio the surrender of Japan in 1945 after the United States had dropped the devastating atom bombs on Hiroshima and Nagasaki.

The novel is set during an unspecified war, when a group of boys from a reformatory are evacuated to a remote Japanese mountain village where they are detested by the local people. The narrator, who is never named, is one of these boys. They are forced to bury animals which, unknown to them, have died of plague. When the plague breaks out, the villagers flee, leaving the boys in the empty village, terrified that they too will develop the disease. Also left behind is a soldier who is in hiding, a young girl who would not leave her dead mother, and a Korean boy called Li. The boys find food and establish some kind of order, and the narrator's younger brother finds a stray dog, which he names Leo and comes to love deeply. This fragile order threatens to break down when the girl whom the narrator has befriended develops plague. There is mounting hostility between the narrator and another boy, Minami, rather like that between Jack and Ralph in *Lord of the Flies*. In the following extract, the boys have found out that the girl has the plague and the narrator is trying to keep their seething terror under control.

Nip the Buds, Shoot the Kids

The comrades were sitting around the fire with sunken heads. I grew anxious when I saw my brother standing apart from their circle with his back turned defiantly towards them, hugging Leo. Minami stood up, took one step towards us and looked Li and me straight in the eyes. His lips were quivering. When he opened his mouth, swallowing spittle, I had an urge to restrain him. But it was too late.

'According to the soldier's diagnosis,' he said hastily, 'it looks like that girl's got the plague.'

Plague: that word. The word that immediately spread its leaves and roots wide all over the village, raging like a tempest, crushing everyone in its path, was shouted out from his throat, becoming reality for the first time in that village where children had been left behind alone. I felt it agitate the boys sitting round the fire, causing a sudden panic.

'That's a lie,' I shouted. 'It's a lie.'

'I kept quiet until you came back,' Minami shouted. 'I swear the soldier told me so clearly. She's got the plague.'

I saw the younger boys suddenly seized by fits of panic and I punched Minami's twitching throat hard. He fell down on the snow that had been melted by the fire and groaned, clutching his throat with both hands. Li held me back as I was about to kick his gut while he struggled for breath. Li's arm was brawny and hot. I stared at the comrades as they stood round the fire, trembling with sudden fright.

'It's not plague,' I said. But fear had soaked deep into them, and they wouldn't listen to me.

'Let's run for it, or we'll die as well,' a scared voice said. 'Go on, take us along, let's run for it.'

'I said it's not plague. Keep on whining, if you want to get punched,' I shouted, raising my voice to conceal the terror which had begun to infect me as well. 'There's no plague here.'

'I know,' another high-pitched voice said frantically. 'She caught the plague from the dog.'

I looked at my brother and Leo in astonishment. My brother turned his back on us, trying even harder to ignore the shouting, and pressed Leo's head against his chest.

'We know as well,' other boys said as if in unison. 'It's the fault of your brother's dog and you're concealing it.'

I was dazed, confronted for the first time by comrades who were against me.

'What's the dog done?' Li said in a sharp, terse voice. 'Eh? What's he done?'

'That dog dug up the bodies,' a tearful voice said weakly. 'Your brother buried them again. We saw him washing his hands and the dog's body. It's been ill ever since. And this morning it bit the girl's arm and gave her the disease. That's why the plague's broken out.'

The end of the boy's sentence dissolved into sobs. I was completely at a loss, and couldn't think about anything else but talking to my brother, who stubbornly kept his back to us.

'Hey, is it true about the dog? It's a lie, isn't it?'

Turning round into the comrades' gaze, my brother tried to move his lips, then looked down in silence. I groaned. The comrades surrounded him and the dog. Tucking his tail between his legs and pressing his shoulder against my brother's knee, the dog looked up at us.

'It's got the plague,' Minami said hoarsely. 'Though you tried to cover it up, we're sure that it gave the plague to the girl.'

'Everyone saw it bite her wrist,' said a comrade. 'Even though she wasn't doing anything, it bit her. It's mad.'

'He's not mad,' my brother protested strongly. He was desperate to protect his dog. 'Leo hasn't got the plague.'

'What do you know; what do you really know about plague?' Minami said, persistently harassing him. 'It's your fault that the plague's broken out.'

My brother endured it all with his eyes wide open and his lips trembling. Then he yelled, clearly trying to suppress the anxiety which he was drawing back from.

'I don't know, but Leo hasn't got the plague.'

'Liar,' voices rebuked him. 'Everyone'll die because of your dog.'

Minami ran out of the circle of accusation and pulled up the green oak branch that the cooking pot was hanging from. Everyone was taken aback, and the circle widened.

'Stop it,' my brother shouted in terror. 'If you hit my Leo, I'll never forgive you.'

But Minami advanced implacably, and whistled sharply. Slipping through my brother's hands as he hastily bent down, the dog came forward, lured by the whistle. I saw my brother turn his imploring eyes towards me, but what could I do? The dog stood awkwardly, hanging out his tongue which looked even to me like a mass of fiercely multiplying germs.

'Li,' my brother shouted, but Li didn't move.

The oak branch came down, and the dog collapsed on the snow with a thud. We all looked at it in silence. Biting his lip, eyes full of tears, his body shaken by sobs, my brother started to stagger forward. But he couldn't look down at the twitching dog, whose black blood was gently soaking the fur over its ears. Shattered by rage and grief, he stirred and spoke.

'Who knew if Leo had the plague? Hey, all of you, who knew?'

He ran off sobbing, head down. Everyone gazed after his small shoulders that were shaking with sobs. I shouted to call him back, but he didn't return. I've betrayed my brother, I thought. How could I console my brother as he lay sobbing, burying his head in the dark granary's musty straw?

Perhaps I should have followed him and comforted him, hugging his shoulders. It might have been the best thing to do; but I had to stop the panic which had seized the younger boys and which might drive them into screaming hysteria. And I thought that now, while they were standing in shock with the poleaxed dog before them, was the best and probably the only opportunity left.

'You,' I shouted. 'Anyone who whines about plague, I'll smash their head in just like the dog. All right? I promise, the plague hasn't broken out.'

They fell silent, disheartened. They were obedient, cowed by the bloody oak bough in Minami's arms rather than my voice. Feeling I had succeeded, I repeated emphatically:

'All right, there's no plague or anything.'

Then I picked up my brother's necklace of pheasant feathers, covered with mud and snow, from where he had been sitting and put it in my coat pocket. Li and Minami threw the dog's carcass on the fire and piled wood on top of it. The weakened fire didn't burn up strongly and the dog's legs stuck out from the firewood for a long time.

'You lot,' I said to the younger comrades in a commanding tone, 'Go back and sleep. I'll hit anyone who makes a fuss.'

Minami looked at me with mocking eyes. That exasperated me.

'Minami, you go to bed too.'

'I won't take orders,' he said, showing hostility. He gripped the oak branch, which was smeared with the dog's hair and blood.

'You should go home,' Li said, eyeing Minami's oak bough. 'If you don't like it, you'll have me to deal with too.'

Minami twisted his face, pushed the oak branch into the fire and yelled at the comrades. 'Anyone who doesn't want to die alone like a dog, come 'n sleep with me. There's germs swarming all around those two.'

Li and I lingered by the fire, scorching our foreheads in the heat, and saw off the others, who had grown anxious and were running after Minami. At first there was the low dry sound of the flames. After that the fat melted and flowed, burning with a sizzling noise, sparks popped up, the thick smell of burning lumps of meat rose and stuck in the air around us. It wasn't the odour, lively and energetic, which had arisen when we roasted the pigeons, the shrikes and the pheasant, but the heavy taste of death. I bent over and vomited up some stubs of vegetables, rice grains, and hard tendons of bird meat. As I wiped my mouth with the back of my hand, Li gazed at me with eyes hollow with fatigue. Exhaustion flowed from them into my body like floodwater and jostled under my skin. I was so exhausted that I found it hard even to straighten up, and very sleepy. And I couldn't bear to stand in the smell of the burning dog any longer. I got up slowly, biting my lips, nodded to Li and turned my back on the fire. I wanted to sleep in the straw by my brother's side like a baby animal. My brother would forgive me, tired out as I was with a heart full of tears: these were sweet thoughts. The moon was hiding behind thick clouds and gave a pearly lustre to their distant rims. The snow had frozen again on the dark road and I felt it creaking under my soles. I went up the slope, the skin of my cheeks numb with cold.

Kenzaburo Oë

Assignments

1 Explain how the tension mounts in this scene.

This is a straightforward question which asks you to look closely at the tension in the scene.
To help you organize your answer, we'll divide the scene up into four parts:
⊕ the effect of Minami's announcement that the girl has the plague
⊕ the young boys' shifting the blame on to the dog
⊕ the killing of Leo and its effect
⊕ the conflict between Minami and the narrator.

Plague

Read the passage carefully and as you read, write down notes on
the tension under each of these headings. Write down brief
quotations to back up what you say.
The first heading has been done for you:

The effect of Minami's announcement that the girl has the plague:
When Minami announces the word they were so frightened of, 'plague', the
tension mounts.
The word is 'crushing everyone in its path'. That adds to the tension because it
makes us feel that all the children are going to be crushed and die.
It gets more tense when the younger boys start to panic, because things are
getting out of control.
There's more drama and tension when the narrator violently punches Minami
in the throat and Li has to stop him from kicking Minami's 'gut'.
'fear had soaked deep' into the children. This terror is in the narrator too and
makes him violent. You don't know what will happen next and this makes it
tense and frightening.

Using your notes, write a paragraph on each heading. Don't forget
to use your quotations as evidence. When you have completed all
four, you will have your full answer to the question.

2 Analyse the effectiveness of the following extracts.

   a *The word that immediately spread its leaves and roots wide all over the
   village, raging like a tempest, crushing everyone in its path, was shouted
   out from his throat, becoming a reality for the first time in that village
   where children had been left behind alone.*

   b *Plague: that word.*

   c *'It's not the plague,' I said. But fear had soaked deep into them, and they
   wouldn't listen to me.*

   d *But he couldn't look down at the twitching dog, whose black blood was
   gently soaking the fur over its ears. Shattered by rage and grief, he
   stirred and spoke.*
   'Who knew if Leo had the plague? Hey, all of you, who knew?'

   e *Minami looked at me with mocking eyes. That exasperated me.*
   'Minami, you go to bed too.'
   'I won't take orders,' he said, showing hostility.

In this question, you are going to **analyse the effectiveness** of some of the lines in the passage.

This means you'll be:

⊕ looking closely at the writer's language and sentence structure

⊕ explaining how they convey the meaning and atmosphere to you, the reader.

Some of the sort of features you'll be looking for are:

⊕ a striking metaphor or simile: does it make the atmosphere more frightening by referring to something terrifying?

⊕ use of direct speech: does it make the scene more dramatic for the reader?

⊕ a short sentence: does it add tension or drama?

⊕ verbs: do they add to the violence or fear?

Look for features like these and explain how well they convey meaning and atmosphere.

The first one has been done for you:

a The sentence is very long and explains how the word 'plague' spreads out through the village. The length of the sentence is like the sweeping movement of the plague so the reader can feel the movement. The way the word 'plague' spreads is 'like a tempest'. This simile conveys well the idea of how powerful the word is. It can destroy things just like a tempest. The writer makes the word sound like a tree or plant in the metaphor 'spread its leaves and roots'. The word, like the plague, spreads and is impossible for people to control.

Now, write about the other extracts in a similar way, and then you have completed the question.

In the Congo
Democratic Republic of Congo

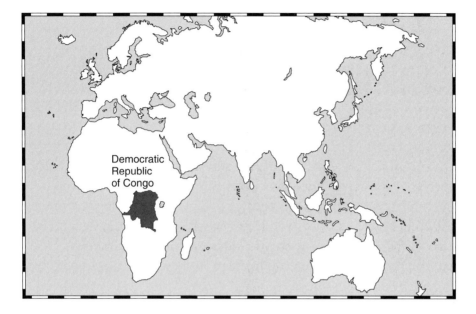

Introduction for the Teacher

This extract is from *The Poisonwood Bible*, a novel set in 1959, in the part of Africa which was then ruled by Belgium, and known as the Belgian Congo. Following the end of colonial rule, it was called Zaire. After the end of Mobutu's rule in 1997, Zaire was renamed the Democratic Republic of Congo.

Nathan Price is a fiercely determined Evangelical Baptist Minister who has come in 1959 from America to bring Christianity to the Belgian Congo. He is not alone, but has brought his long-suffering wife and four daughters who have to adjust to living in a bare wooden house in the heart of Africa. At first, the children find everything entirely alien – and the Congolese think the family extremely strange, especially the youngest girl, Rachel, with her very pale blonde hair.

When the Belgians withdraw from the territory in 1960, violence erupts as the tribal chiefs and the leaders of the rival political movements vie for supremacy. The Baptist Minister refuses to return with his family to America with the Europeans, obliging them all to suffer the terrors and increasing dangers of the ensuing turbulence.

In this part of the story, Leah Price, the eldest sister, describes her impressions of the village and its people. Her job is to look after the youngest sister, five-year-old Ruth May, and not let her stray from the compound around their house, but Leah finds this restricting and dull. She terrifies her little sister into staying in the compound by telling her a snake will kill her if she ventures out, so that she herself can go out and explore.

The Poisonwood Bible

As soon as I had her good and terrified I'd slip away. I'd go hunt for the Pygmies, who are supposed to be dwelling right under our noses in the forest, or for monkeys (easier to spot). Or I'd cut up fruit for Methuselah[1], still hanging around begging, and catch grasshoppers for Leon, the chameleon we keep in a wooden crate. Mother lets us keep him on the condition we never bring him in the house. Which is funny, because I *found* him inside the house. His bulging eye sockets swivel whichever way they please, and we love to get his eyes going so one looks up and the other down. He catches the grasshoppers we throw in his box by whipping out his tongue like a slingshot.

I could also try to talk Father into letting me tag along with *him*. There was always that possibility. Father spends his days making rounds through the village, trying to strike up chats with the idle old men, or venturing farther afield to inspect the state of grace in the neighbouring villages. There are several little settlements within a day's walk, but I'm sorry to report they all fall under the jurisdiction of our same godless chief, Tata Ndu.

Father never lets me go that far, but I beg him anyhow. I try to avoid the drudgery of housekeeping chores, which is more up Rachel's alley *if* she can stoop to being helpful on a given day. My view of the home is, it is always better to be outside. So I loiter at the edge of the village, waiting for Father's return. There, where the dirt road makes a deep red cut between high yellow walls of grass, you never know what might be coming toward you on dusty feet. Women, usually, carrying the world on their heads: a huge glass demijohn full of palm wine, with a calabash bowl[2]

---

[1] Methuselah: the children's pet bird
[2] calabash bowl: bowl made from a large gourd

perched on top like an upside-down hat; or a bundle of firewood tied up with elephant grass, topped off with a big enamel tub full of greens. The Congolese sense of balance is spectacular.

Most of the girls my age, or even younger, have babies. They appear way too young to be married, till you look in their eyes. Then you'll see it. Their eyes look happy and sad at the same time, but unexcited by anything, shifting easily off to the side as if they've already seen most of what there is. *Married* eyes. And the younger girls – if they are too young to be married and too old to be strapped on someone's back (which is not a wide margin) – why, they come striding along swinging their woven bags over their shoulders and scowl at you, as if to say, Out of my road, can't you see I'm busy! They may only be little girls tagging after their mothers, but believe you me, with them it's all business. The girls are usually just about bald, like the boys. (Mother says it's from not getting their proteins.) But you can tell the girls by their stained, frilly dresses, castoffs from some distant land. It took me aback for months that they look so much like little boys in ruffly dresses. No girl or woman wears pants, *ever*. We are the odd birds here. Apparently they think we're boys, except maybe Rachel, and can't tell a one of us apart from the other. They call us all *Beelezi*, which means Belgians! I mean to tell you, they call us that right to our faces. It's how they greet us: '*Mbote, Beelezi!*' The women smile, but then cover their mouths, embarrassed. The little babies take one look and burst out crying. It's enough to give you a complex. But I don't care, I'm too fascinated to hide indoors or stay cooped up in our yard. Curiosity killed the cat, I know, but I try to land on my feet.

Right smack in the middle of the village is a huge kapok tree, which is where they get together and have their market every fifth day. Oh, that's something to see! All the ladies come to sell and bicker. They might have green bananas, pink bananas, mounds of rice and other whitish things piled on paper, onions or carrots or even peanuts if it's our lucky day, or bowls of little red tomatoes, misshapen things but highly prized. You might even see bottles of bright orange soda pop that someone walked here all the way from Leopoldville, I guess, and will walk a long way more before they're all sold. There's a lady that sells cubes of caramel-coloured

soap that look good to eat. (Ruth May snitched one and took a
bite, then cried hard, not so much from the bad taste as the
disappointment, I imagine. There's so little here for a child in the
way of sweets.) Also sometimes we'll see a witch doctor with
aspirins, pink pills, yellow pills, and animal pieces all laid out in
neat rows on a black velvet cloth. He listens to your ailments,
then tells you whether you need to buy a pill, a good-luck charm,
or just go home and forget about it. That's a market day for you.
So far we've only purchased things from around the edges; we
can't get up the nerve to walk in there whole hog and do our
shopping. But it's fascinating to look down the rows and see all
those long-legged women in their colourful *pagnes*[1], bent over
almost double to inspect things laid out on the ground. And
women pulling their lips up to their noses when they reach out to
take your money. You watch all that noise and business, then look
past them to the rolling green hills in the distance, with antelopes
grazing under flat-topped trees, and it doesn't fit together. It's like
two strange movies running at the same time.

On the other days when there's no market, people just congregate
in the main square for one thing and another: hairdos, shoe repair,
or just gossiping in the shade. There's a tailor who sets up his foot-
pedal sewing machine under the tree and takes their orders, simple
as that. Hairdos are another matter, surprisingly complicated, given
that the women have no real hair to speak of. They get it divided
into rows of long parts in very intricate patterns so their heads end
up looking like balls of dark wool made of a hundred pieces, very
fancily stitched together. If they've got an inch or two to work with,
the hairdresser will wrap sprigs of it in black thread so it stands up in
little spikes, like Mama Boanda Number Two's. The hairdo business
always draws an audience. The motto seems to be, If you can't grow
your own, supervise somebody else's. The elderly women and men
look on, working their gums, dressed in clothes exactly the same
colour as their skin, from all the many ground-in years of wash and
wear. From a distance you can't tell they have on anything at all, but
just the faintest shadow of snow-white hair as if Jack Frost lightly

---

[1] pagne: a length of cloth tied around the waist to make a skirt

touched down on their heads. They look as old as the world. Any colourful thing they might hold in their hands, like a plastic bucket, stands out strangely. Their appearance doesn't sit square with the modern world.

Mama Lo is the main hairdresser. She also runs a palm-oil business on the side, getting little boys to squash it out of the little red oil-palm nuts in her homemade press and selling it to the other villagers just a little each day, for frying their greens and what not. Mama Lo doesn't have any husband, though she's as industrious as the day is long. With the way they do here, it seems like some fellow would snap her up as a valuable add-on to his family. She isn't a whole lot to look at, I'll grant you, with her sad little eyes and wrinkled mouth she keeps shut, morning till night, while she does everybody's hair. The state of her own hair is a mystery, since she always wraps her head in a dazzling cloth printed with peacock feathers. Those lively feathers don't really match her personality, but like Tata Boanda in his ladies'-wear sweater, she seems unaware that her outfit is ironic.

Barbara Kingsolver

Assignments

1 What impression does the writer give of Leah's character?

First of all, you need to read the passage. It is written in the first person with Leah as the 'I'. As you read it, make a list of Leah's qualities of character. You will need to **interpret** some of her words and actions to find some of the qualities. Write a quotation to illustrate each quality on your list.

The list has been started for you:

> 1 *inquisitive and curious: 'I'm too fascinated to hide indoors or stay cooped up in our yard.'*
>
> 2 _____
>
> 3 _____
>
> 4 _____
>
> 5 _____

Now for the next step. In a paragraph, explain fully the quality of character in detail, making further references to the text. The first one has been done for you:

> *Leah is very curious about her surroundings and is keen to explore: 'I'm too fascinated to hide indoors or stay cooped up in our yard.'*
>
> *The way she begs her father to be allowed to go with him on his rounds to the neighbouring villages shows that she wants to find out more and she sounds intrigued, not at all frightened, by the 'godless chief, Tata Ndu.' Housekeeping to her is 'drudgery' because she wants to be out exploring.*

When you have written a paragraph on each of the qualities on your list, you have completed the whole question.

2 How does the writer use language to convey Leah's impressions of her new home?

This question is really asking you to do two things:
⊕ identify the language used to convey Leah's impressions
⊕ explain **how** it conveys Leah's impressions.

To organize your response, we'll make some headings for you to focus on:
⊕ the colours in Leah's surroundings
⊕ the different movements and activities going on
⊕ Leah's impressions of the children and young girls
⊕ the description of the natural scenery.

Read the passage and as you read, write down notes and quotations under each heading. Your first set of notes might look like this:

> **The colours in Leah's surroundings**
> *the red of the road and the 'high yellow walls of grass';*
> *the brightly coloured fruit: green and pink bananas, red tomatoes, 'whitish things';*
> *orange soda pop; caramel-coloured soap;*
> *the witch doctor's pink and yellow pills on black velvet cloth.*

Now you are ready for the second part of the question:

Explain **how** the language conveys Leah's impressions.

The language doesn't just describe the scene, but lets you see it through Leah's eyes. To answer this part of the question, you need to **analyse** the words and sentence structure in the notes you have made so that you can explain how this is done. The sort of features you should be looking at are:

⊕ exclamation marks: what do they tell you about Leah's impressions of the place?
⊕ brackets and dashes: how do these convey Leah's impressions?
⊕ listing: what is the effect of describing in this way?
⊕ vocabulary: what is the effect of words conveying colour, or of American words and phrases?
⊕ personal pronouns: what is the effect of using 'you'?

Now, write a paragraph on each of the headings in which you **analyse** the language in this way. When you have done that, you have answered the question in full.

Persian Bazaar
Iran

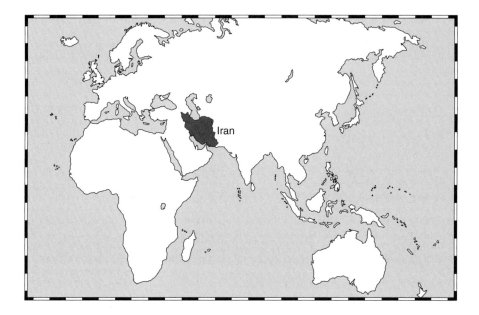

Introduction for the Teacher

The author of the next extract, Sattareh Farman Farmaian, was born in Shiraz in Persia (as Iran was then known) in 1920 where her father was a military commander related to the ruling family of Qajar Shahs, or Emperors. He was sixty when Sattareh, or Satti as she was affectionately called, was born to the third of his eight wives – the fifteenth of his thirty-six children. At that time, the country was ruled by the Qajar dynasty, but in 1921 there was a *coup d'état* and Reza Khan, an army Commander, came to power as Prime Minister and later proclaimed himself Shah of Iran.

Sattareh's father knew that he and his family would be safe only if he made no trouble for the new regime. He established them all in the capital, Tehran, in a compound surrounded by beautiful gardens and pools which had belonged to the deposed Qajars. Sattareh's childhood spent there was a protected, happy one surrounded by over thirty brothers and sisters and a thousand servants. Her father was unusually enlightened for a Moslem at that time and believed that education for daughters was all-important. Sattereh later studied in America, and returned to found the Tehran School of Social Work.

In this extract, she describes the childhood ritual she loved: visiting the market with her favourite house servant or *laleh*, Mashti.

Daughter of Persia

On Saturday, the first day of the week, and on every other morning except Friday, I would hear my laleh's big voice bellowing from our gatehouse as I sat on the dining room carpet gulping down my boiled milk. 'Come on, Satti-Khanom[1], you're late! Come on, Farough Mirza, hurry up – everyone is waiting!'

I and my next younger brother, Farough – despite our father's orders to the contrary, the servants all called him 'Farough Mirza,' or 'Prince Farough' – would choke down the rest of our food and my mother would yell out the window, 'Just a minute, Mashti, I'm fixing their snack.' Then she would hastily roll some cheese into a bit of soft bread or tie a few handfuls of nuts and raisins into our handkerchiefs. As soon as she shoved them into our pockets we would scuttle down the staircase and out the path to the gatehouse where Mashti would be waiting, along with Batul-Khanom's son Abol, Fatimeh-Khanom's sons Ali-Naghi and Ali-Dad, and his own daughter Leila and some of the other servants' youngsters, to march us all off to Tarbiat Elementary School, which was down the street.

Mashti had come into my father's service at about the time I was born, and now served my mother as gatehouse watchman, baby-sitter, and general errand boy. He was also our escort and bodyguard whenever we needed to leave home to go to school, the bazaar, or a relative's house. Mashti was the strongest man in the entire compound and could lift furniture and carpets that no one else could budge. His hands, jutting like spades from the sleeves of his blue cotton tunic, were long-fingered and muscular, and his broad face and shiny, nearly bald head were as brown as walnut juice from the sun. He only called me 'Satti-Khanom,' Lady Satti, when my mother was in earshot. The rest of the time I was just 'Satti'.

I loved Mashti! I was tremendously proud of his strapping shoulders and brawny, sunburnt forearms, his big moustache and

---

[1] Khanom: respectful title for a female, Lady

large kind eyes and flashing smile. We had been companions since I was old enough to walk. On weekdays he inhabited the gatehouse, where he had a tiny private room that held his bedding, clothes, and a small wooden chest for things like tobacco and matches. In cold weather we would often sit together for hours in the antechamber of the gatehouse, talking like two old chums and warming our hands and feet at his charcoal brazier. While I was still small enough, he used to hoist me onto his back or put me into the long wrought-iron shoulder basket he took to market when he shopped for my mother's groceries, and I would swing along beside him, wild with delight, he grinning at my ecstasy. Often, when we were at the market, seeing me gaze wistfully at the sticky, fly-covered candies at the confectioner's stall (both my mother and Shazdeh[1] had expressly forbidden us these vermin-specked treats), he would hand the stall's proprietor one or two of his own hard-earned pennies to buy me a few, whispering in my ear, 'Don't tell Khanom, or she'll eat my bald head for supper.' Although I loved Shazdeh passionately, I felt with equal conviction that I was Mashti's daughter as well, though in a different way. When I visited the little house across from the compound where Mashti lived with his pretty wife Korsum and their three children, or rode to school on his shoulders or walked beside him to the market, I could imagine what it must be like to belong to a family of ordinary people and have a man live at home with us, someone whom I could hug and talk to and call 'Father.' I yearned to call Shazdeh 'Father' instead of 'Ghorban[2],' to throw my arms around his waist and bury my face in his tummy, as I had seem Mashti's daughter Leila do with my laleh.

Unfortunately, even though my mother was very fond of Mashti, she also considered him a sort of emissary from heaven – one whom God had sent to add to her burdens and thus teach her the virtue of patience. Not only did Mashti, in her view, let me and my brothers run wild in the biruni[3], but he also let us drink filthy street water and fed me the confectioner's dirty candies. The fact that Shazdeh might get word that she had let him do these

[1] Shazdeh: Satti's father, who was called by the title of Shazdeh, meaning Shah's son
[2] Ghorban: term of extreme respect
[3] biruni: outside part of the compound, for men

things was at least as significant to Khanom as the distinct possibility that we might catch typhoid, dysentery, or roundworm. But worst of all, my laleh was a terrible shopper.

Mashti invariably lugged home in his iron basket the very worst fruits and vegetables the vendors could palm off on him. Agriculture in Iran was poor like everything else, and the grocers, to make their wares go farther, cheated their customers shamelessly. Frequently, a perfectly fresh bunch of onions or a sound apple or a healthy radish would disappear behind the stallkeeper's scales to be weighed, bagged, and presented to the customer with a hundred polite Persian exclamations of gratitude and indebtedness, only to turn up in my mother's courtyard kitchen as a wormy apple, a black radish, or a rotten handful of onions.

Needless to say, my mother did not have money to waste on inferior or spoiled food. She would have been glad to send someone besides Mashti, who was too simple and trusting to spot a trick coming. But there was no one else to send. So, every day when he went off to shop, she would say, 'Mashti, when you go to the market today, make sure that the fruit dealer gives you his best goods. For heaven's sake, try to *notice* what he's giving you – don't use just two eyes, use four!'

But Mashti's open, unsuspecting nature completely nullified whatever protection four eyes might have given him. Every day he came home with soft cucumbers or spoiled turnips, and every day my mother would storm across the courtyard to the gatehouse to bawl him out through the curtain that screened the andarum[1] from the gatekeeper's view, shouting as loudly as her strict modesty permitted, 'Mashti, I send you to buy a watermelon and you come back with something that is not red inside but white, like a cabbage! You know the children can't eat this thing! How can you waste our money this way? Do you think Shazdeh is going to give me more just because Mashti is such a fool that he doesn't know a good watermelon from a bad one?'

'Khanom,' Mashti would plead, 'it's not my fault – the man swore to me it was a good one. Some *jinni* – '

---

[1] andarum: inner part on the compound, for women

'Spirits have no influence over watermelons,' snapped my mother, more irritated that ever. Superstition was another thing Shazdeh had forbidden.

'But, Khanom,' Mashti protested humbly, 'how was I to know it was bad? I was not *inside* the watermelon.'

'God be praised forever and give me patience,' my mother would exclaim. 'If Mashti did not go to the bazaar, all the rotten fruit dealers in Iran would be out of business.'

'There is just no justice, Satti,' Mashti would say glumly when we were alone, shaking his head and puffing on one of the cigarettes I liked to roll for him. 'Your mother, a saintly and generous woman, is pleased to think that I carelessly brought home a bad watermelon. All I know is, it was good when I picked it out. Well, by God's will it turned out to be a bad one after all. Either I was cheated, or the watermelon was good when I bought it and bad when it came home. It was not my fault, it was fate. Who can argue with that?'

Mashti and all the servants and my mother as well believed that everything was in the hand of heaven. If you sat under a pomegranate tree and a piece of fruit fell into your lap, it fell not because of some force called gravity but because God had willed that the fruit should fall at that particular moment. And if something good or bad fell into your lap, that too was ordained. Scarcely a day passed in which Mashti and fate did not have an encounter of this kind, which Mashti usually lost.

Fortunately, my laleh could never be angry for long, and soon he would cheer up. 'God the Compassionate and Merciful sees everything,' he would tell me soberly, 'and always punishes the wicked. Nothing on earth gets past God, who is everywhere, and who made the cow that causes earthquakes by shaking her head and tossing the earth between her horns. If you do something bad, not even hiding in the privy can protect you, because God is everywhere and sees everything. But God protects the victims of injustice. He is the avenger of wrongs. Wait and see – I will pray for that fruit dealer to be punished, and God will have him eaten by a desert ghoul.'

Sattareh Farman Farmaian

Assignments

---

1 Why was young Satti so fond of her laleh, Mashti?

Satti was obviously very fond of Mashti so you'll be able to find plenty of reasons. To organize your answer, we'll make four headings for you to focus on:
⊕ Mashti's strength
⊕ Satti's visits to the gatehouse and to Mashti's home
⊕ Satti's trips to the bazaar with Mashti
⊕ Mashti's role as father figure to Satti.

Read the passage and as you read, write down what it was about each topic that made little Satti so fond of Mashti. Include brief quotations as well as your own words.
Now you are ready to write up your findings into paragraphs. Remember, don't just describe what happened, but explain **why** she was so fond of him.
The first one has been written for you:

> *Mashti was 'the strongest man in the entire compound' and could lift things no-one else could. Satti loved him for this strength, shown in his huge hands which jutted 'like spades' from his sleeves and had muscular, strong fingers. She was 'tremendously proud' of his 'strapping shoulders and brawny, sunburnt forearms' and he was like a huge hero to her. Not only was he admirably powerful and strong; he also was affectionate towards her and had a huge 'flashing smile'.*

When you have written a paragraph on each of the headings, you have completed the question.

2 How does the writer convey the contrast between Mashti and Satti's mother, Khanom?

Mashti and Khanom are obviously very different in their temperaments and in what they believe. The writer conveys this contrast in the incidents she writes about, and in the language she uses. To organize your answer, we'll make headings, two focusing on the content of the passage, and two on the writer's words and sentence structure:

Content:
- Mashti's shopping skills compared with Khanom's
- Mashti's philosophy of why things happen compared with Khanom's.

Language:
- how the words show the contrast between Khanom's and Mashti's temperaments
- how the punctuation in Khanom's and Mashti's speech shows their different personalities.

Read the passage and then write a paragraph on each heading, using the following to help you:

Content:
- **Mashti's shopping skills compared with Khanom's**
  What were the effects of Mashti's 'unsuspecting nature'?
  What did Khanom suspect of the stall holders?
- **Mashti's philosophy of why things happen compared with Khanom's**
  What did Mashti believe happened to the watermelon?
  What did Mashti and Khanom believe about fate?
  What was Khanom's view of superstition?

Language:

⊕ **how the words show the contrast between Khanom's and Mashti's temperaments**

When Mashti and Khanom have a conversation, the writer uses different words instead of 'he said' or 'she said'. Look at the words she uses for Mashti's speech, and those she uses for Khanom's. What differences do they show between the speakers?

⊕ **how the punctuation in Khanom's and Mashti's speech shows their different personalities**

In different colours for Khanom's and Mashti's speech, write out the sentences that end in exclamation marks and those that end in question marks. What is the effect of this different punctuation?

What does the dash after he says *jinni* show about Khanom?

When you have used these questions to write a full paragraph on each of the headings, you have completed the whole question.

A Truck Ride from Hell

Afghanistan

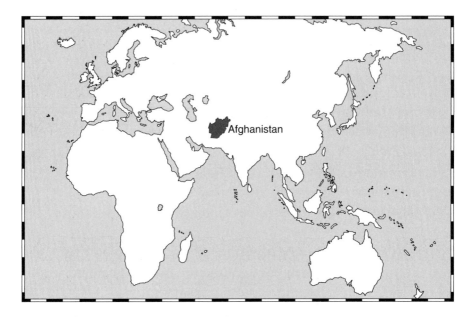

Introduction for the Teacher

The borders of landlocked Afghanistan are with Pakistan, Iran and Russia. From 1979-1989 Afghanistan was the arena of an immensely destructive war in which Soviet Russia tried to prevent the Communist regime in Afghanistan being overthrown by various tribal and Islamic resistance movements known as the Mujaheddin. As a young man of nineteen, before going to University, Jason Elliot was drawn to Kabul, the capital, where the fighting was at its height, to see the country and the war for himself. He spent several months with the Mujaheddin during which time he developed a deep sympathy with the suffering of the Afghan people.

Ten years later, in 1995, Elliot returned to the country and travelled extensively by truck and on horseback on fascinating but often extremely dangerous journeys. The Soviets had withdrawn, but a civil war was going on between different elements of the Mujaheddin. Shelling was still going on spasmodically, and unexploded mines lay in wait to kill and maim. Since 1995 the country has been mostly under the power of the Taliban, an extreme Islamist group, who have restored law and order but have also imposed severe laws such as forbidding girls to go to school and women to go to work. However, in northern Afghanistan where Elliot was travelling, the Taliban were still strongly opposed and tribal factions continued to fight against them and each other.

An Unexpected Light is a brilliant account of Elliot's travels and reflections on the country and its people. The extract is from the first part of a perilous truck ride from Faizabad in north east Afghanistan, several hundred miles to the ancient city of Mazar-i Sharif. Before leaving Faizabad, Elliot had asked the driver what the condition of the road ahead was like. The answer had not been encouraging: 'Ruined! So many trucks fall off into the river. So many are killed.' Nevertheless, the 'kamaz', the giant truck, was loaded with goat skins, heavy engine parts, eight people including Elliot – and a live sheep. With a shriek of the horn and amidst prayers of supplication, it set off, blasting black exhaust into the street.

An Unexpected Light: Travels in Afghanistan

We had not yet reached the edge of the town before the first floundering. A government fighter flagged down the truck just as we crossed the river, and insisted on inspecting the cargo. Under the conditions of the time it was the nature of such interruptions to be drawn out and resolved not so much by a logical solution, but by a protracted fraying of tempers and an eventual consensus of pointlessness. So it was with our marooning; a wearying ritual obeisance to the Gods of war.

The fighter was young and seemed uncertain of his task. He shouldered his rifle and clambered up the back of the truck, studied our faces in turn and began to poke about among the engine parts and goat skins, asking repeated questions from their owner. Then, unsatisfied with the explanations, he ordered us all out of the truck.

First went the women, incongruously balloon-like against the sharp angles of the truck, with all but their bare hands hidden by elaborately embroidered *burqas*[1] of cornflower-blue silk. An elderly turbaned gentleman in a dark corduroy jacket followed them, helped by the fighter; then a ginger-haired man wearing a black fur hat; a patriarchal whitebeard clutching a trembling crook; a stocky, bearded man with mirrored sunglasses and what

---

[1] *burqas*: wide flowing robes that cover everything but the eyes and hands

looked like a tea towel over his head; a pair of Turcoman-looking traders whose goatskins it appeared were the cause of the hold-up, and finally the sheep, a huge creature with mad-looking horizontal pupils and great wedge-shaped tail like a flipper, which shook in protest as it was manhandled to the ground.

There were long arguments between the soldier and the owner of the skins. Other passengers interjected voluble protests in turn, which drew out into counter-protests and a general rising in temperature of the debate. The driver, and even passers-by, entered the fray. I wandered away. A military jeep with a 'GB' sticker drove past, followed by an old man on a donkey. Then a boy chasing a metal hoop, guided with deft blows from a hooked bar. I noticed too, at the exact height of the driver's head, a bullet-hole in the windscreen of the truck.

An hour had passed before the owner of the skins, with a conspicuous show of exasperation, began flinging them one by one down into the road, where they threw up little clouds of dust at the soldier's feet. But after only a dozen or so the scale of the task became apparent to all – there must have been hundreds of skins on board – and a renewed cry of protest rippled through the stranded assembly. Then, as if the whole thing had never mattered to him, the soldier wandered grudgingly away, and with a wail of the horn we were all hastily reinstalled.

The road led west in the shadow of a steep bluff of dark rock, and soon we were in the open, overlooked by soft hills. Homes sprawled around their bases, and directly above them, rocks as big as the houses themselves, anchored to the slopes by no more than slender collars of mud.

Our way was paved with the pure and ochreous light of the season. The houses trailed behind us and we passed the airport, where a truckload of armed teenage boys were filing like cattle up the ramp of a military plane. Even at a distance I could make out their smiles as they prepared to set off for the front lines around Kabul, and the sight fell across my feelings the way a cloud obscures the sun on a Spring day.

Not far beyond, the surface of the road began to break up like the fraying end of a rope. Soon it was raked with deep and interweaving ruts of frozen mud. Our pace dropped to a crawl, and the frame of the truck began to sway and creak like an old galleon in a rising storm.

I was standing behind the cab and watching the route ahead, gripping the metal crossbars like a charioteer. This was not the Afghan way, which was less ostentatious. The other passengers, long immune to the novelty and risks of open-air travel on ruined roads, huddled stoically against the sides. The exception was the man with the sunglasses. He too stood at the truck's edge and watched the road. With his beard and scarf and his face set against the wind, he looked more suited to the saddle of a Harley Davidson. There was something about him I couldn't place, and for once I was doing the guessing about someone else.

It was mid-afternoon. Already the sunlight like a tide had begun to slip back from the hills, and as we entered a wide gorge enclosed by high walls of broken rock its touch was withdrawn from our faces. The temperature began to fall and the road tightened against the cliff. We lurched forward, rising steadily, over braided furrows of mud as the note of strain from the engine began to grow, and before long we were steering between fallen boulders on one side and the deepening gorge on the other.

The road narrowed, too, as it rose. It was high and broken enough for even the steadiest nerves, but now its ruined surface began to curve and bend and fold, fractal-like[1], hanging from the cliff-face in tortured pleats. I looked out over the wheels to see how much space we had to bargain with, and with a sick feeling saw the tyres bulging at the very edge of the cliff. The river coiled a hundred, then two, then three hundred feet below, without so much as a handhold on the intervening slope. On the nearside of the road side rose a sheer wall of rock, inches from the body of the truck.

As we climbed, the cry of the engine grew more desperate. There were two sounds now; the first, a kind of wail, bleeding

---

[1] fractal-like: like a complex pattern which folds around itself but is never exactly repeated

from the heart of the engine as it begged to be allowed into a higher gear. Then over this, the heavy growl of the cylinders under enormous strain. It was like riding a mechanized dragon caught at the end of a lasso, its brute determination transmitted to every seam and rivet. A hot breath of black exhaust, as dense as it was noxious, billowed from underneath us. It rolled upwards against the cliff then down again over the body of the truck where we clung, our mouths clenched.

It was getting dark and I began to wonder how long we could possibly continue. But darkness was no obstacle to the iron nerves of the driver, whose accomplice, a teenage boy, would lean from the open door of the cab like a sidecar racer and look out over the rear wheels at the most dangerous points, yelling directions back over the roar of the engine. Soon all but a dusty yellow swathe of road in the headlights was obscured by the darkness. I wasn't sure which was better; not to be able to see ahead and give up all chance of making a last-minute escape, or to forgo this tiny insurance for the relative relief of not knowing at all.

I was on the side nearest the precipice, and worked on a mental plan of escape. At the moment we began to topple over the cliff, I would swing to the far side on the central bar of the canopy and jump free just in time. This would mean using the women opposite me as a kind of stepping-stone, and I abandoned the plan out of shame. But it was a pointless plan; firstly because if the wheels did slip, there would simply be no time for anything; secondly because I could not keep up the anxiety of thinking about the consequences. You can only be afraid for so long; after a long mental battering you are eventually forced inwardly to that deeper and stranger place to which fear is only an overdressed guard at the portal.

Often the driver would bring the truck to a complete halt as he decided how to attack the next section of road. In the back we could see nothing of the road now, but sensed these momentary pauses as the preludes to the most dangerous sections, like hairpin bends where the camber sloped horribly towards the cliff, or where the road had been partially washed away and was supported only by loose rocks plugged with broken sticks. Then we would hear the preparatory bursts of throttle, the screeching into first gear, and the old man in the back would croak: 'a prayer, a prayer!' and our palms would turn heavenward through the dust as we banged against the metal frame, too cold now even to grip.

The sheep, traumatized by the terrible ride, became demented. It refused to sit, despite being wrestled time and again to its knees. It staggered and fell repeatedly against us in turn, pissed in straggling arcs of terror over our feet until the canvas was awash, and trailed cascades of droppings as it bounced like an ice-hockey puck from side to side and end to end, its eyes ever madder with distress. At one point I forced it to lie down, and for a long stretch warmed my feet under its stomach. Then at another violent tilting of the truck it would repeat its frantic efforts to stay upright until finally, hours later, it grew too exhausted to care.

In the west a sickle moon hung like a nomad earring over the vee of the valley. Its cold light was reflected from the river like the scales of a writhing mercury snake. Under its silver spell our dusty faces – except those of the women, who stayed hidden like treasure under their *burqas* – took on the ashen hue of corpses. Mantra-like, I heard the words I had been left with in Faizabad: *so many trucks are falling off… so many are dying…*

I knew I had to find some method to distract from the fear.

Jason Elliot

Assignments

1 Describe the behaviour of the writer's fellow passengers, including the sheep, on the journey. What do the reminders of war add to the atmosphere?

The question is in two parts. We'll start with the first part:

Describe the behaviour of the writer's fellow passengers, including the sheep, on the journey.

This is straightforward question which asks you to select the relevant material from the passage relating to:
- the other human passengers
- the sheep.

Make two columns, a 'human passengers' column and a 'sheep' column. Read the passage and as you read, take notes on their behaviour and quote appropriate phrases. The lists have been started for you:

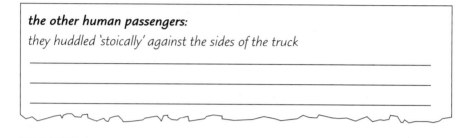

the other human passengers:
they huddled 'stoically' against the sides of the truck
_____
_____
_____

the sheep:
the poor sheep was 'traumatized' and 'demented' by the journey
_____
_____
_____

Now use your notes to write a paragraph on each and then you are ready for the next part:

What do the reminders of war add to the atmosphere?

To organize your response, we'll focus on two points:
- the government fighter inspecting the load
- the activity at the airport.

Read the first six paragraphs of the passage again. For this part of the question, you are not asked to describe, but to explain how these parts add to the atmosphere. Focus on:
- drama
- tension
- the writer's feelings.

Write a paragraph on each and you have then completed the whole question.

2 Explain clearly the meaning of the following extracts, commenting on the effect of the words used.

a *First went the women, incongruously balloon-like against the sharp angles of the truck, with all but their bare hands hidden by elaborately embroidered burqas of cornflower-blue silk.*

b *Our pace dropped to a crawl, and the frame of the truck began to sway and creak like an old galleon in a rising storm.*

c *It was like riding a mechanized dragon caught at the end of a lasso, its brute determination transmitted to every seam and rivet. A hot breath of black exhaust, as dense as it was noxious, billowed from underneath us.*

d *In the west a sickle moon hung like a nomad earring over the vee of the valley. Its cold light was reflected from the river like the scales of a writhing mercury snake.*

For the first part of the question, you need to write down what you understand the lines to mean. In the second part you are going to comment on the effect of particular words and phrases. The sort of features you will look at are:

⊕ similes and metaphors: is one used for a particular effect?
⊕ words suggesting colour: are the colours significant in any way?
⊕ adjectives: what do they add to the description?
⊕ verbs: do they perhaps add to the drama?

The first one has been answered for you:

The women get down from the truck, and their brightly-coloured clothes are puffed out by the wind. The phrase 'balloon-like' reinforces the contrast with the 'sharp angles of the truck' – the clothes stress the women's softness and make the truck seem all the harder. The writer dwells on their 'elaborately embroidered' silk burqas to stress how feminine they seem, and their strong colour, 'cornflower-blue', suggests a beauty that further contrasts with the wretched atmosphere of the passage.

Write a paragraph like this on the other extracts, and then you have completed the question.

Desert Crossing
Iran

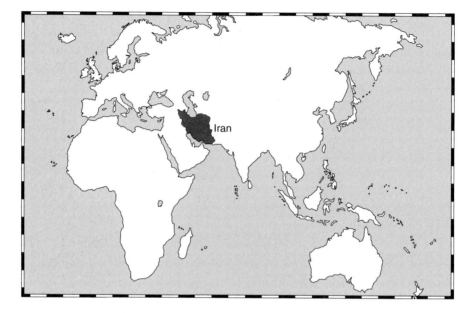

Introduction for the Teacher

This extract comes from a very remarkable book by Vincent Cronin. He was fascinated by the travel writings of the sixteenth century merchant and traveller, Anthony Jenkinson. Jenkinson had written intriguingly about the 'pasturing people' of Persia, and Cronin resolved to travel to Persia (as Iran was then called) and find out more about these nomadic tribes. Travelling in that part of the world was not easy in the very early 1950's. Not only did he travel there by an immensely difficult and complex overland route but, in order to meet the nomadic Kashgai tribal people in whom he was interested, he had to have letters of introduction and the required passes which were very difficult to obtain.

As part of Reza Shah's plans for establishing a New Iran when he came to power in 1925, these ancient nomadic people had been settled by law. Being nomadic, they had never lived in one place for any length of time before and many of the tribespeople died in these enforced settlements. It was not until Reza Shah's abdication in 1941 that their then depleted numbers were free to resume their ancient nomadic traditions. Vincent Cronin realized his ambitions and lived amongst the Kashgai people for a whole year.

[136]

The Last Migration is, in Persian tradition, a *dastan*, a piece of 'near-factual history'. For the purpose of his story, he renamed the Kashgai tribe of central Persia the Falqani and called their *Ilkhan*, their Leader, Ghazan. This extract is the dramatic account of Ghazan's spiritual pilgrimage from Yezd to Meshed across the Dasht-i-Lut, the desert, which is the dry heart of Persia whipped by a scorching wind called the simoom. On the pilgrimage across the desert, Ghazan took with him only his servant Ahmad, two horses and two goatskins of water. They took barley for their horses and rice and dates for themselves. It was to be a hellish journey.

The Last Migration

Next morning, their fifth in the desert, Ghazan woke to find Ahmad haggard, his black-bearded face drawn. All night he had been too frightened to close his eyes, and spoke only of jinns. Ghazan had to force him to mount, then spoke of things they could both see, peculiar-shaped stones or a stunted tamarisk growing between white streaks of salt. Ahmad sat hunched on his grey horse, silent and white-cheeked. He seemed infected by the mildewed, leprous waste.

Towards midday, without a word, Ahmad put heels to his horse and swung round at a canter southwards. At once Ghazan followed, shouting at him to stop. In three hundred paces Ghazan's faster horse had brought them level. Dropping his reins Ghazan lunged and seized Ahmad by the waist. His servant slipped free with a twist which shook off his hat. They galloped on, manœuvring. Ghazan caught Ahmad by the tunic collar and drew both horses to a trot. Ahmad still struggled wildly. The strain drew his saddle sideways; a cord snapped and the full goatskin of water flopped to the ground. Both riders turned and drew up. The wooden plug had been forced out and water was spurting on to the sand with a gurgling sound. Ghazan leaped off his horse and ran to the fallen goatskin. By the time he had replaced the stopper, the goatskin hung loose and lifeless.

He rounded on Ahmad. 'Idiot!' he shouted in fury. 'Son of a burned father! Brilliant heir to a long line of asses and goats! Cross the desert without water would you, you camel!'

He called his servant every outrageous name he could think of. Ahmad seemed not to hear. He dismounted and stood staring at

[137]

the pattern of darker brown, the water's own grave. Kneeling, he grovelled with his finger-tips in the wet sand, trying to save a few drops. Then he buried his face in his hands and sobbed. Beside the slowly shrinking stain a few salt tears fell.

The goatskin on Ghazan's horse was half-empty. Hardly ten mouthfuls remained in the other. With strict rationing they had five days' water for themselves and their beasts – just about enough to carry them across the desert. It would be safer to retrace their steps – Ghazan knew that – but pilgrims could not lightly turn their back on Meshed. He decided to continue.

Visible danger seemed to have shocked Ahmad back to his senses. For hours he rode quietly beside Ghazan. Under the hot sun they were like two pots in the firing-oven. No shadow, not even a fly's. They had forgone their noon drink; soon their mouths were parched. When they spoke, it was always about the lost water.

In the late afternoon Ghazan saw ahead a shimmering, silver-white expanse distinct from the dusty beige sand and the blue sky. Soon trees appeared on the far shore, reflected in its surface. Ahmad saw it too and they agreed it must be an illusion. They occurred even in bare tribal country, and Ghazan had already alerted his mind against them.

But as they rode on and still the water shimmered, Ghazan began to succumb to the desire of his dry throat and the evidence of his eyes. They couldn't be distrusted for long: they accurately reflected his clothes and saddle-bags, Ahmad and his grey horse. They might be mistaken about a few drops, he argued, but not about this vast expanse. He had heard of no inland lakes, but the desert was unexplored. Unknown water, and if it were fresh! It lay at least two hours away: time to dash in often, feel the cool liquid over his legs, splash it over his dusty hair, wash and drink. They rehearsed how best to enjoy it. But the lake lay further than they had imagined. Finally they marked it by a nearby bluff. Still they talked of water: grey and black as it gurgled out of a newly greased goatskin, the mud-coloured rain which fell near the Gulf, pink water in redstone hills, the bottled tasteless water of Teheran. And their eyes remained fixed on the shimmering undeniable expanse ahead.

They passed the bluff and agreed they must have mistaken their marker, for the lake still lay far. Again they marked the lake. All afternoon they rode through the dusty sand until the sun had sunk almost to the horizon. Suddenly, before their watching eyes, like mist or a rainbow, the lake vanished. Desert on all sides. They had crossed it as the Israelites crossed the Red Sea. At first they could not believe it, then in a rush of disappointment they filled their parched mouths from Ghazan's goatskin.

Ghazan puzzled over the incident. He had seen water and walked over the dry place where water had been. Surely no dew fell on this wilderness. Had he divined an underground lake? Or seen the wet film over his own eyes? And why did he come upon such lakes so unexpectedly, like a dream after many dreamless nights? Yet this had been no dream. And the lakes were never found on uneven ground or tilted: they obeyed all laws but the fundamental law of contradiction. Perhaps the sun-entranced earth could produce water for a time on its surface, just as fakirs could by force of will produce running welts on their skin. Till late he discussed the water with Ahmad. On one point they agreed: these imaginary lakes where they took imaginary baths and drinks were remembered long after draughts of real water; invented to satisfy the thirst of the mind, they endured – as though compensating for their non-existence.

On the eighth day a sandstorm blew up out of nowhere, breaking the desert silence with a whirling sound and the skidding of grit against salt rock. Earth and sky intermingled; the flat surface became so many moving mountains, and it was they who had to be still. Dismounting, they made their horses lie and crouched behind them. Puny things, kneeling for mercy before the hot wind: how different, thought Ghazan, from that saint for whom the simoom was more pleasant than a spring breeze, who stood on burning sand as though on silk or broidered cloths. For himself, he could not rise above his discomfort: howled back curses at the wind. The dust suffocated them and rasped their throats. Into their ears and under their fingernails the burning sand swept, prising their bodies apart. For several hours they lay like this: gasping, dry as cinders, half-buried by the air.

The whine softened to a hum, the hum to silence. Stumbling to their feet, they shook grit from hair and beards, gulped a mouthful of water and gave to their horses. The dunes had changed outline, the sand had effaced their tracks and thick dust obscured the sun. Each day they had started with the sun at their right shoulder and after noon kept it behind them to the left. Now they had to guess at their route and, making up lost time, to march under a starless light.

That afternoon their minds no less than their bodies began to suffer from thirst. Ghazan felt a wild urge to spit at the sun, to extinguish it. Ahmad began to chant confused snatches of verses against jinns. Once more he spoke of riding towards the heart of the desert: now Ghazan shared his fear and knew what he was trying to flee. He attached a cord to the bit of Ahmad's slow-stepping horse, and held the end with his own reins.

Next morning, as Ahmad was mounting, his horse sank to the ground. From sheer exhaustion all four legs had buckled. Milk of the Moon was also weak: she hung her head and her eyes were dull. There was nothing for it but to lead the horses and stagger along on foot. The sharp gravel soon tore their cord shoes; their feet dragged naked along the blistering sand, each step an ordeal by fire. Ahmad began to shout for water, then start to scoop up the sand. This tortured Ghazan as much as heat and thirst. It made the journey and its purpose seem idiotic. His throat was so dry, he could not speak the sane phrases which would combat the nonsense. He felt drawn into the delirium. Death, he thought – let that be, if it has to be, but without the preamble of madness.

By the evening of the eleventh day their mouths and throats had become raw flesh lashed by every breath of the salt air. Ahmad raved no longer – he had no more saliva; from time to time he grunted. Head to foot they flopped down on the sand, without fire or food, for they had finished their last dates that morning. Weary from hunger and the long day's march, Ghazan slept soon, but very fitfully. During the night he thought he heard one of the horses neighing.

At dawn he woke to find Ahmad already up. Nearby glowed the embers of a tamarisk fire. Strange, he thought, and strange too that Ahmad eyed him aslant. Then with a start he noticed behind the near shoulder of Ahmad's grey horse a wound, dressed with ashes. He was certain it hadn't been there last night. What could have caused it? He examined the wound: straight and deep, as though a vein had been opened. He turned quickly. Ahmad, who had been watching, dropped his eyes. Tense with suspicion, Ghazan unbuckled the saddle-bag and found Ahmad's gourd. Brown with dry blood. He looked in horror at Ahmad, clothes ragged, beard unkempt, blackened by the sun. God forgive us, thought Ghazan, thirst has sent him sprawling down the centuries to this – worse than the worst long-forgotten orgies. He seized Ahmad's shoulder. 'Not again – never,' he whispered, shaking a fist.

Ghazan plodded on, conscious only of his movement, of the steps which sent his brain burning.

Through his dry eyes it became painful to see visions and nightmares struck from the burning sand and his burning brain. He closed his eyes and walked blindly, following the sun like some primitive organism without eyes, yet bound to move towards the light. He had become indifferent to their survival: only this twitching of his limbs continued, which he likened to the nervous spasm of a newly slaughtered sheep. Moments of clearness would intrude, when he sensed his predicament: unbearably intense, but short. His breath seemed to him a two-handled saw, pulled this way and that, cutting down the tree of existence.

In one of these lucid intervals he saw what he took to be yet another mirage, a line of figures moving far away across their own direction. He pointed them out to Ahmad, who nodded as if he saw them too. Many times they had stumbled towards figures to find them cairns erected who knew when: but these past experiences were already blurred and did not check similar new ones.

It struck Ghazan that these shapes were odd. They cast no reflection. They moved. They were of different size: some high, long and humped; others lower and thin. A red daub, then a blue on the grey-brown canvas. Presently Ghazan saw the outlines of many camels, riders perched behind the humps, moving north, a long line of words writing their reprieve across the sand.

He felt no joy: only a painful transition to the key of hope.

Their steps now had a purpose, but unless they hurried, the caravan would pass without noticing them. Two days' fast had weakened their legs, and their efforts at running were monstrous. They flung up their arms in grotesque scarecrow gestures, opened full their mouths and lungs and cried no louder than sparrows in the nest. Steadily the caravan filed past. They had not been spotted. So close, yet they had not been spotted. They were nothing, they were dead, they did not exist: this was the proof.

Walking, they could not catch up with the camel train, yet instinctively, like jackals, they followed the tracks, watching the figures seep like water into the desert, sink with all their hopes, with life itself, beyond the horizon. Ghazan wanted to weep. His eyes twitched but, as though pain had exhausted all stores of grief, not one tear came from his dry body. He was an empty coconut, hay, shell of a shellfish, dust: a wisp in the hot wind.

They staggered forward in starts, walking to the limit of their strength, then flopping on their knees to rest. The horizon was bare now except for one black patch. A cairn to mark their grave. As they approached, it bifurcated. Two cairns for two graves. They limped on, from surprise to surprise. One was too high, one too large to be a pile of stones. But this seemed scarcely to matter. Nothing mattered.

Presently there could be no doubt at all: the cairns were a man and a camel, stationary. Ghazan waved and cried. The man turned and walked towards them. Ghazan saw eyes, nose and mouth take shape. Reality was too much for him. He fell reeling to the ground.

Vincent Cronin

Assignments

1 Explain the difficulties which Ghazan and Ahmad experienced as they crossed the desert with their horses.

This was such a terrible journey that there's certainly no shortage of material for this question! To organize your answer, we'll focus on four episodes from the journey:

- the spilling of the water
- the mirages
- the collapse of the horse
- the sandstorm.

Read the passage and as you read, take notes under these headings. Then using these notes, write a paragraph. In it, don't just describe what happened, but explain the significance of the difficulties as well.

The first one has been done for you:

> *Ahmad was terrified after a night spent awake in fear, and was in a physically poor state: 'silent and white-cheeked'. He ran off 'without a word', and the goatskin was lost when Ghazan struggled with him, trying to bring him back to his senses. The stain left on the ground that the men stared at is called 'the water's own grave', which suggests that the loss of water might have dire consequences.*

When you have written a paragraph on each episode, you have finished the whole question.

---

2 How does the writer make the final section of the story dramatic? (from 'At dawn he woke to find Ahmad already up' to the end of the passage.)

What happens in this section is extremely dramatic. To help you answer the question, we'll divide it into three scenes:

- Ahmad's crime
- Ghazan's terminal suffering
- the appearance of the caravan and their final rescue.

First of all, read the section of the passage and make sure you know exactly what happened in each of these scenes. Now, we need to consider the **how** part of the question:

How does the writer make the final section of the story dramatic?

The writer's tools for making the scenes dramatic are:
- sentence structure and punctuation
- similes and metaphorical language
- vivid nouns, adjectives, verbs and adverbs.

Look at each scene in turn and find examples from the features above which contribute to its dramatic force. Write a few sentences in which you explain how this dramatic effect is obtained in each of your examples.
The first scene has been done for you:

> 'Brown with dried blood' – this short phrase stands on its own as a dramatic sentence. It is effective because it contrasts with the longer sentences. It conveys dramatically Ahmad's shocked horror as he finds confirmation of what he suspected – that his servant has been driven to the crime of drinking his horse's blood.
>
> 'thirst has sent him sprawling down the centuries to this' – this is a dramatic image of Ahmad's offence. The metaphor presents Ahmad as dramatically falling down a pit into an uncivilized past when such terrible crimes were committed. 'Sprawling' suggests that he has slipped down the pit, which emphasizes his helplessness without water.
>
> 'Clothes ragged, beard unkempt, blackened by the sun' – the way the writer uses a string of adjectives makes the description more dramatic because it builds up a powerful description of Ahmad's physical deterioration. The adjectives – 'ragged', 'unkempt' and 'blackened' – have two syllables which draws out the description still further and the consonants are hard, to show the disgust and horror of the situation.

When you have completed a paragraph on each of the other scenes, you have completed the whole question.